DEPARTMENT OF HEALTH & HUMAN SERVICES

Maternal and Child Health Bureau

Administration

Rockville MD 20857

Dear Colleague:

The Health Resources and Services Administration's (HRSA) Maternal and Child Health Bureau (MCHB) is pleased to present Stepping Stones to Using Caring for Our Children, 2nd Edition. The second edition of Stepping Stones was developed from the comprehensive document Caring for Our Children: National Health and Safety Performance Standards: Guidelines for Out-of-Home Child Care Programs, 2nd Ed. to identify those standards most needed to prevent disease, disability and death in child care settings.

The goal of this document is to support State licensing and regulatory agencies, public and private child care entities, parents, health care professionals and organizations, resource and referral agencies, and early care and education advocacy groups in their efforts to achieve improved health and safety in child care.

Under a 5 year cooperative agreement awarded to the National Resource Center for Health and Safety in Child Care (NRC), HRSA's MCHB supported NRC to develop the second edition of Stepping Stones. Stepping Stones and Caring for Our Children are both available on the NRC web site, http:// nrc.uchsc.edu.

Staff and I encourage you to continue to use Caring for Our Children, 2nd Edition as the comprehensive resource document it is intended to be. MCHB hopes you will find Stepping Stones, 2nd Ed. to be a valuable resource in developing policies and regulations, particularly as you plan and provide for the health and safety of children in child care settings.

Sincerely yours,

Peter C. van Dyck, M.D., M.P.H.
Associate Administrator for Maternal
and Child Health

# PLEASE BE ADVISED:

Changes in health practice that have occurred since the publication of the second editions of

*Caring for Our Children*

and

*Stepping Stones to Using Caring for Our Children*

can be found online at

**http://nrc.uchsc.edu/CFOC/updates.htm**

# STEPPING STONES
## TO USING
## CARING FOR OUR
## CHILDREN:

National Health and Safety Performance Standards:
Guidelines for Out-of-Home Child Care Programs
Second Edition

Caring for Our Children is a Joint Collaborative Project of

American Academy of Pediatrics
141 Northwest Point Blvd.
Elk Grove Village, IL  60007-1098

American Public Health Association
8001 I Street, N.W.
Washington, DC  20001-3710

National Resource Center for Health and Safety in Child Care
University of Colorado Health Sciences Center at Fitzsimons
Campus Mail Stop F541, PO Box 6508
Aurora, CO  80045-0508

Support for this project was provided by the
Maternal and Child Health Bureau,
Health Resources and Services Administration,
Department of Health and Human Services
(Cooperative Agreement # U93 MC 00098)

ISBN   0-9715682-1-9 (National Resource Center for Health and Safety in Child Care)

AVAILABILITY:
*Stepping Stones, 2nd Ed.* and *Caring for Our Children: National Health and Safety Performance Standards: Guidelines for Out-of-Home Child Care Programs, 2nd Ed.* are available as full text on the Web site of the MCHB supported National Resource Center for Health and Safety in Child Care (http://nrc.uchsc.edu).

Print copies of the comprehensive source document *Caring for Our Children: National Health and Safety Performance Standards: Guidelines for Out-of-Home Child Care Programs, 2nd Ed.* are available from the American Academy of Pediatrics and the American Public Health Association. See Appendix BB for contact information.

Printed and bound in the United States of America
        Design: Kathy Duran, David Merten
        Typesetting: David Merten

# TABLE OF CONTENTS

(Editor's Note: *Stepping Stones, 2nd Edition* only includes those appendices directly mentioned in the text of the included standards, all others are located in *Caring for Our Children, 2nd Edition*.)

# ACKNOWLEDGMENTS

The National Resource Center for Health and Safety in Child Care would like to acknowledge the outstanding contributions of all persons and organizations involved in the revision of *Stepping Stones to Caring for Our Children, Second Edition.* The collaboration of the American Academy of Pediatrics, the American Public Health Association, and the Maternal and Child Health Bureau provided a wide scope of technical expertise from their constituents in the creation of this project. The subject-specific Technical Panels provided the majority of the content and resources. Over 40 organizations were asked to review and validate the accuracy of the content and contribute additional expertise where applicable. See Contributors on page 147 for a listing of the Technical Panel Chairs and Members and individuals representing the organizations which gave valuable input. This broad collaboration has led to a more comprehensive and useful tool.

## Steering Committee

### Susan S. Aronson, MD, FAAP
Co-Chair, American Academy of Pediatrics, PA

### Albert Chang, MD, MPH, FAAP
Co-Chair, American Public Health Association, CA

### Phyllis E. Stubbs-Wynn, MD, MPH
Chief Infant and Early Childhood Branch, Department of Health and Human Services, Health Resources and Services Administration, Maternal and Child Health Bureau, DC

### Marilyn J. Krajicek, EdD, RN, FAAN
Director, National Resource Center for Health and Safety in Child Care, CO

### Barbara U. Hamilton, MA
Assistant Director, National Resource Center for Health and Safety in Child Care, CO

# INTRODUCTION

The first edition of *Caring for Our Children: National Health and Safety Performance Standards: Guidelines for Out-of-Home Child Care Programs (CFOC)* was published in 1992.  Professionals in the fields of early education and health quickly embraced the standards as effective tools to improve health and safety in early education and child care programs. The 981 standards in *CFOC, 1st edition* provided a comprehensive blueprint for quality. After the publication of the standards, some users asked the experts to identify a subset of the standards linked to the most serious risks so that they could begin their use of *CFOC* with this subset as a priority. In 1997, the National Resource Center for Health and Safety in Child Care published the 1st edition of *Stepping Stones to Using Caring for Our Children* as a companion document. The selected standards were those most likely to prevent frequent or severe disease, disability and death (morbidity and mortality) in child care settings. Subsequently, many public and private organizations such as state child care, health, and resource and referral agencies, as well as a variety of professionals who work in child care settings, parents, and advocacy groups have used *Stepping Stones* to target limited resources to these priority standards.

*Caring for Our Children: National Health and Safety Performance Standards: Guidelines for Out-of-Home Child Care Programs* was revised extensively from 1997-2001. The Maternal and Child Health Bureau (MCHB) funded the revision process that involved updating, consolidating and adding standards as appropriate. The resulting document contains 659 standards. The American Academy of Pediatrics (AAP), the American Public Health Association (APHA), and the National Resource Center for Health and Safety in Child Care (NRC) jointly published *CFOC, 2nd Edition* in 2002. To reflect the many changes/additions to *CFOC, 2nd Edition* content, NRC worked with the Steering Committee for *CFOC, 2nd Edition* to implement a process for revising *Stepping Stones* that was completed in 2003. Using the same criteria to select standards for the 2nd edition as for the first edition of *Stepping Stones*, 233 standards in *CFOC, 2nd Edition* were identified as having the greatest impact on reducing frequent or severe disease, disability and death (morbidity and mortality) in early education and child care settings.

The steps followed to select the standards for *Stepping Stones, 2nd Edition* included:
- Field-based informants were interviewed to identify significant problems in health and safety practice that are covered in *CFOC*, but were not included in *Stepping Stones, 1st Edition;*
- Fifty-five experts from 10 technical subject areas (experts who had developed the content for *CFOC, 2nd Edition*) rated the risk of harm to children and child care staff for noncompliance with specific standards. The experts reviewed the standards they had developed that were in the 1st edition of *Stepping Stones* and those that had been identified by field-based informants;
- Users of *Stepping Stones, 1st Edition* were surveyed on methods to enhance the format and usability of *Stepping Stones, 2nd Edition;* and
- National organizations, representing providers, parents, child care advocates, health professionals, safety specialists, early childhood educators, regulators, and federal, military, and state agencies that promote and implement quality and safety in the field of early education and child care, were asked for feedback on the standards and enhancements in the format suggested by the previous steps.

## CHANGES

The NRC enabled discussions to establish among the participants wherever possible and the Steering Committee decided which arguments for changes for the 2nd edition were persuasive. The significant content and format changes and additions for this new edition of *Stepping Stones* are:
- Addition of new standards on sleep position of infants related to SIDS studies; oral health requirements; outdoor play temperature conditions; training on standard precautions; handling and feeding of human milk; care of children with asthma and with food allergies; availability of water in daily program activities and for supply in disasters; installation of safety devices to reduce risks of finger pinching;
- Integration of standards throughout the document that are relevant to children with special needs, as well as to all children, to promote inclusion;
- Arrangement of standards in the same order as they appear in the *CFOC, 2nd Edition*

Our sincere appreciation goes to all of our colleagues who willingly gave their time and expertise to the development of this resource. Please see Acknowledgements on page v and a listing of all contributors on page 147 and Advice to Users on page x for more information on intended audiences and uses. We hope this latest offering provides the support and assistance needed to improve the health and safety of children in early education and child care settings.

Susan S. Aronson, MD, FAAP
Albert Chang, MD, MPH, FAAP
Co-Chairs, Steering Committee

Phyllis E. Stubbs-Wynn, MD, MPH
Project Officer and Chief, Infant and Early Childhood Branch
Department of Health and Human Services
Health Resources and Services Administration
Maternal and Child Health Bureau, DC

Marilyn J. Krajicek, EdD, RN, FAAN; Director
Barbara U. Hamilton, MA; Assistant Director
National Resource Center for Health and Safety in Child Care
Aurora, CO

# ADVICE TO USERS

*Stepping Stones, 2nd Edition contains* 233 standards selected as a subset of the 659 national health and safety performance standards in *Caring For Our Children, 2nd Edition (CFOC).* This subset includes the standards that have the greatest impact on disease, disability and death (morbidity and mortality) in out-of-home child care. To keep the document size manageable, *Stepping Stones, 2nd Edition* contains only the unaltered text of the selected standards without the rationale, comments or references and only those appendices directly mentioned in the text of the included standards.

Editor's notes indicate corrections required since *CFOC, 2nd Edition* was published. Many pertinent references appear in the rationale in *CFOC, 2nd Edition* and are therefore not included in *Stepping Stones, 2nd Edition.* Useful appendices that are not directly referenced in the text of the cited standards can be found in *CFOC, 2nd Edition.* Please consult the hard copy or the Internet version of *Caring For Our Children, 2nd Edition (CFOC)* at http://nrc.uchsc.edu for the rationale, comments, references, cross-referenced standards and full set of appendices.

In *Stepping Stones,* numbering of references in the text of the standards and numbering of appendices appears verbatim as in *CFOC, 2nd Edition,* even though the references are not listed in *Stepping Stones.* Some users may have difficulty locating some of the references in scientific journals. The staff of the National Resource Center for Health and Safety in Child Care will help locate copies of cited references and address questions about how to use the print and Internet versions of *CFOC, 2nd Edition* and *Stepping Stones, 2nd Edition.*

## INTENDED AUDIENCES AND USES

Many users may find the *Stepping Stones* useful in promoting health and safety of children in early education and child care environments:

   State licensing and regulatory agencies - to identify the standards for comparison with and improvement of state child care policies, practices, and regulations.
   Child care providers - to improve the quality of child care operations and environment.

Parents – to inform and educate on health and safety features that they should look for in their child's early education and child care setting.

Resource and referral agencies – to advise parents and providers of important performance issues for quality child care.

Communities - to implement the Healthy Child Care America Campaign with its 10-Step *Blueprint for Action*. The Campaign promotes a partnership of families, child care and health care providers to support the healthy development of young children in child care and increase access to preventive health services and safe physical environments. Contact information on the Healthy Child Care America Campaign can be found in Appendix BB.

## FORMAT AND ORGANIZATION

The standards in *Caring for Our Children: National Health and Safety Performance Standards for Out-of-Home Child Care Programs, 2nd Edition (CFOC, 2nd Edition)*, are numbered according to the chapter in which they are located. The same numbering system has been used for the 233 standards included in *Stepping Stones, 2nd Edition* to assist users in correlating the two documents. Chapter titles and associated numbering are:

Staffing (Standard numbers starting with 1)

Program: Activities for Healthy Development (Standard numbers starting with 2)

Health Protection and Health Promotion (Standard numbers starting with 3)

Nutrition and Food Service (Standard numbers starting with 4)

Facilities, Supplies, Equipment and Transportation (Standard numbers starting with 5)

Infectious Diseases (Standard numbers starting with 6)

Children Who are Eligible for Services Under IDEA (Standard numbers starting with 7)

Administration (Standard numbers starting with 8)

As is true in *CFOC, 2nd Edition*, standards in this book have application to three types of out-of-home child care settings. Each standard in *Stepping Stones, 2nd Edition* lists which type of child care facility for which the standard is applicable. These are:

A **Small Family Child Care Home** provides care and education for up to six children at one time, including the preschool children of the caregiver, in a residence that is usually, but not necessarily, the home of the caregiver. The key elements are that this type of care takes place in a setting that is used both for child care and as a residence (often simultaneously) and that the total number of children is limited to a maximum of six at any one time. Family members or other helpers may be involved in assisting the caregiver, but often, there is only one caregiver present at any one time.

A **Large Family Child Care Home** provides care and education for between 7 and 12 children at a time, including the preschool children of the caregiver, in a residence that is usually, but not necessarily, the home of one of the caregivers. Staffing of this facility involves one or more qualified adult assistants so that the requirements specified in the child:staff ratio and group size standard are met. The key element that distinguishes this type of facility is the combined use of the premises as a residence and for child care (often simultaneously) and that the number of children in care requires more than one caregiver present at any one time.

A **Center** is a facility that provides care and education to any number of children in a nonresidential setting, or 13 or more children in any setting, if the facility is open on a regular basis. To distinguish a child care center from drop-in facility, a center usually provides care for some children for more than 30 days per year per child. In many cases, summer camps operate for more 30 days per year per child and, in fact, provide center-based child care.

# CHAPTER 1 - STAFFING

## STANDARD 1.001
## RATIOS FOR SMALL FAMILY CHILD CARE HOMES

The small family child care home provider child:staff ratios shall conform to the following table:

| **If** the small family child care home provider has no children under two years of age in care, | **then** the small family child care home provider may have 1-6 children over two years of age in care |
|---|---|
| **If** the small family child care home provider has 1 child under two years of age in care, | **then** the small family child care home provider may have 1-3 children over two years of age in care |
| **If** the small family child care home provider has 2 children under two years of age in care, | **then** the small family child care home provider may have no children over two years of age in care |

The small family child care home provider's own children shall be included in the child:staff ratio.

TYPE OF FACILITY: *Small Family Child Care Home*

## STANDARD 1.002
## RATIOS FOR LARGE FAMILY CHILD CARE HOMES AND CENTERS

Child:staff ratios in centers and large family child care homes shall be maintained as follows during all hours of operation, including transport and nap times:

| Age | Maximum Child:Staff Ratio | Maximum Group Size |
|---|---|---|
| Birth - 12 mos. | 3:1 | 6 |
| 13 - 30 mos. | 4:1 | 8 |
| 31 - 35 mos. | 5:1 | 10 |
| 3-year-olds | 7:1 | 14 |
| 4-year-olds | 8:1 | 16 |
| 5-year-olds | 8:1 | 16 |
| 6 - 8-year-olds | 10:1 | 20 |
| 9 - 12-year-olds | 12:1 | 24 |

During nap time, at least one adult shall be physically present in the same space as the children.

Other adults who are included in the child:staff ratio need not be in the same space with the children when all the children are napping. However, in case of emergency, these adults shall be on the same floor and shall have no barrier to their coming to help immediately. The caregiver who is in the same space with the children shall be able to summon these adults without leaving the children.

When there are mixed age groups in the same room, the child:staff ratio and group size shall be consistent with the age of most of the children when no infants or toddlers are in the mixed age group. When infants or toddlers are in the mixed age group, the child:staff ratio and group size for infants and toddlers shall be maintained. In large family child care homes with two or more caregivers caring for no more than 12 children, no more than three children younger than 2 years of age shall be in care.

TYPE OF FACILITY: *Center; Large Family Child Care Home*

Rationale, comments and references for each Standard are located in *Caring for Our Children, 2nd Edition* (http://nrc.uchsc.edu/CFOC/index.html)

## STANDARD 1.003
## RATIOS FOR FACILITIES SERVING CHILDREN WITH SPECIAL HEALTH NEEDS

Facilities enrolling children with special needs shall determine, by an individual assessment of each child's needs, whether the facility requires a lower child:staff ratio.

TYPE OF FACILITY: *Center; Large Family Child Care Home: Small Family Child Care Home*

## STANDARD 1.004
## RATIOS DURING TRANSPORTATION

Child:staff ratios established for out-of-home child care shall be maintained on all transportation the facility provides or arranges. The driver shall not be included in the ratio. No child of any age shall be left unattended in a vehicle.

TYPE OF FACILITY: *Center; Large Family Child Care Home; Small Family Child Care Home*

## STANDARD 1.005
## RATIOS FOR WADING AND SWIMMING

The following child:staff ratios shall apply while children are wading or swimming:

| Developmental Levels | Child:Staff Ratio |
|---|---|
| Infants | 1:1 |
| Toddlers | 1:1 |
| Preschoolers | 4:1 |
| School-age Children | 6:1 |

During any swimming/wading activity involving mixed developmental levels where either an infant or a toddler is present, the ratio shall always be 1 adult to 1 infant/toddler. The required ratio of adults to older children shall be met without including the adults who are required for supervision of infants and/or toddlers. An adult shall remain in direct physical contact with infants at all times during swimming or wading.

TYPE OF FACILITY: *Center; Large Family Child Care Home; Small Family Child Care Home*

## STANDARD 1.008
## REFERENCES AND BACKGROUND CHECKS

Directors of centers and caregivers in large and small family child care homes shall check references and examine employment history and criminal and other appropriate court records (including fingerprinting and checks with state child abuse registries) before employing any staff member (including substitutes), even in states where licensing has not been instituted. Background checks shall be required for all child care providers.

When checking references, prospective employers shall specifically ask about previous convictions with child abuse or child sexual abuse. Failure of the prospective employee to disclose previous convictions of child abuse or child sexual abuse is grounds for dismissal.

Persons who acknowledge being sexually attracted to children or who acknowledge having physically or sexually abused children, or who are known to have committed such acts shall not be hired or allowed to work in the child care facility.

TYPE OF FACILITY: *Center; Large Family Child Care Home; Small Family Child Care Home*

## STANDARD 1.009
## PRESERVICE AND ONGOING STAFF TRAINING

In addition to the credentials listed in STANDARD 1.014, prior to employment, a director of a center or a small family child care home network enrolling 30 or more children shall provide documentation of at least 26 clock hours of training in health, psychosocial, and safety issues for out-of-home child care facilities.

Small family child care home providers shall provide documentation of at least 12 hours of training in child development and health management for out-of-home child care facilities prior to initiating operation.

All directors and caregivers shall document receipt of training that revisits the following topics every 3 years:

a) Child development knowledge and best practice, including knowledge about the developmental stages of each child in care;

b) Child care as a support to parents;

c) Parent relations;

d) Ways that communicable diseases are spread;

e) Procedures for preventing the spread of communicable disease, including handwashing, sanitation, diaper changing, food handling, health department notification of reportable diseases, equipment, toy selection and proper washing, sanitizing to reduce the risk for disease and injury, and health issues related to having pets in the facility;

f) Immunization requirements for children and staff, as defined in STANDARD 1.045;

g) Common childhood illnesses and their management, including child care exclusion policies;

h) Organization of the facility to reduce the risks for illness and injury;

i) Teaching child care staff and children about infection control and injury prevention;

j) Staff occupational health and safety practices, such as proper procedures, in accordance with Occupational Safety and Health Administration (OSHA) bloodborne pathogens regulations;

k) Emergency procedures, as defined in STANDARD 3.048 through STANDARD 3.052;

l) Promotion of health in the child care setting, through compliance with STANDARD 3.001 through STANDARD 3.089;

m) Management of a blocked airway, rescue breathing, and other first aid procedures, as required in STANDARD 1.026;

n) Recognition and reporting of child abuse in compliance with state laws;

o) Nutrition;

p) Knowledge of medication administration policies and practices;

q) Caring for children with special needs in compliance with the Americans with Disabilities Act (ADA);

r) Behavior management.

TYPE OF FACILITY: *Center; Large Family Child Care Home; Small Family Child Care Home*

---

# STANDARD 1.010
## ADDITIONAL QUALIFICATIONS FOR CAREGIVERS SERVING CHILDREN BIRTH TO 35 MONTHS OF AGE

Caregivers shall be prepared to work with infants and toddlers and, when asked, shall be knowledgeable and demonstrate competency in tasks associated with caring for infants and toddlers:
a) Diapering;
b) Bathing;
c) Feeding;
d) Holding;
e) Comforting;
f) Putting babies down to sleep positioned on their backs and on a firm surface to reduce the risk of Sudden Infant Death Syndrome (SIDS);
g) Providing responsive and continuous interpersonal relationships and opportunities for child-initiated activities.

To help manage atypical or disruptive behaviors of children, caregivers, in collaboration with parents, shall seek professional consultation from the child's source of routine health care or a mental health professional.

TYPE OF FACILITY: *Center; Large Family Child Care Home; Small Family Child Care Home*

# STANDARD 1.011
## ADDITIONAL QUALIFICATIONS FOR CAREGIVERS SERVING CHILDREN 3 TO 5 YEARS OF AGE

Caregivers shall demonstrate the ability to apply their knowledge and understanding of the following, to children within the program setting:
a) Typical and atypical development of 3- to 5-year-old children;
b) Social and emotional development of children, including children's development of independence and their ability to adapt to their environment and cope with stress;
c) Cognitive, language, early literacy, and mathematics development of children through activities in the classroom;
d) Cultural backgrounds of the children in the facility's care by demonstrating cultural competence through interactions with children and families and through program activities.

Rationale, comments and references for each Standard are located in *Caring for Our Children, 2nd Edition* (http://nrc.uchsc.edu/CFOC/index.html)

To help manage atypical or disruptive behaviors of children, caregivers, in collaboration with parents, shall seek professional consultation from the child's source of routine health care or a mental health professional.

TYPE OF FACILITY: *Center; Large Family Child Care Home; Small Family Child Care Home*

## STANDARD 1.012
## ADDITIONAL QUALIFICATIONS FOR CAREGIVERS SERVING SCHOOL-AGE CHILDREN

Caregivers shall demonstrate knowledge about and competence with the social and emotional needs and developmental tasks of 5- to 12-year old children, be able to recognize and appropriately manage difficult behaviors, and know how to implement a socially and cognitively enriching program that has been developed with input from parents.

To help manage atypical or disruptive behaviors of children, caregivers, in collaboration with parents, shall seek professional consultation from the child's source of routine health care or a mental health professional.

TYPE OF FACILITY: *Center; Large Family Child Care Home; Small Family Child Care Home*

## STANDARD 1.017
## QUALIFICATIONS OF EDUCATION COORDINATORS, LEAD TEACHERS, AND TEACHERS

Education coordinators, lead teachers, and teachers shall be at least 21 years of age and shall have at least the following education, experience, and skills:
a) A Bachelor's degree in early childhood education, child development, social work, nursing, or other child-related field, or a combination of experience and relevant college coursework;
b) One year or more years of experience, under qualified supervision, working as a teacher serving the ages and developmental abilities of the children in care;
c) On-the-job training to provide a nurturing environment and to meet the child's out-of-home needs;
d) A valid certificate in pediatric first aid, including management of a blocked airway and rescue breathing, as specified in First Aid and CPR, STANDARD 1.026 through STANDARD 1.028;

e) Knowledge of normal child development and early childhood education, as well as knowledge of children who are not developing typically;
f) The ability to respond appropriately to children's needs;
g) The ability to recognize signs of illness and safety hazards;
h) Oral and written communication skills.

Every center, regardless of setting, shall have at least one licensed/certified lead teacher (or mentor teacher) who meets the above requirements working in the child care facility at all times when children are in care.

Additionally, facilities serving children with special needs associated with developmental delay shall have one licensed/certified teacher who is certified in special education.

TYPE OF FACILITY: *Center*

# STANDARD 1.023
# INITIAL ORIENTATION OF ALL STAFF

All new full-time and part-time staff shall be oriented to, and demonstrate knowledge of, the items listed below. The director of any center or large family child care home shall provide this training to all newly hired caregivers before they begin to care for children. For centers, the director shall document, for each new staff member, the topics covered and the dates of orientation training. Staff members shall not be expected to take responsibility for any aspect of care for which their orientation and training have not prepared them.

Small family child care home providers shall avail themselves of orientation training offered by the licensing agency, a resource and referral agency, or other such agency. This training shall include evaluation that involves demonstration of the knowledge and skills covered in the training lesson.

The orientation shall address, at a minimum:
a) Regulatory requirements;
b) The goals and philosophy of the facility;
c) The names and ages of the children for whom the caregiver will be responsible, and their specific developmental needs;
d) Any special adaptation(s) of the facility required for a child with special needs for whom the staff member might be responsible at any time;

Rationale, comments and references for each Standard are located in *Caring for Our Children, 2nd Edition* (http://nrc.uchsc.edu/CFOC/index.html)

e) Any special health or nutrition need(s) of the children assigned to the caregiver;

f) The planned program of activities at the facility. See Program of Developmental Activities, STANDARD 2.001 through STANDARD 2.027;

g) Routines and transitions;

h) Acceptable methods of discipline. See Discipline, STANDARD 2.039 through STANDARD 2.043; and Discipline Policy, STANDARD 8.008 through STANDARD 8.010;

i) Policies and practices of the facility about relating to parents. See Parent Relationships, STANDARD 2.044 through STANDARD 2.057;

j) Meal patterns and food handling policies and practices of the facility. See Plans and Policies for Food Handling, Feeding, and Nutrition, STANDARD 8.035 and STANDARD 8.036; Food Service Records, STANDARD 8.074; Nutrition and Food Service, STANDARD 4.001 through STANDARD 4.070;

k) Occupational health hazards for caregivers, including attention to the physical health and emotional demands of the job and special considerations for pregnant caregivers. See Occupational Hazards, STANDARD 1.048; and *Major Occupational Health Hazards*, Appendix B;

l) Emergency health and safety procedures. See Plan for Urgent Medical Care or Threatening Incidents, STANDARD 8.022 and STANDARD 8.023; and Emergency Procedures, STANDARD 3.048 through STANDARD 3.052;

m) General health and safety policies and procedures, including but not limited to the following:

1) Handwashing techniques and indications for handwashing. See Handwashing, STANDARD 3.020 through STANDARD 3.024;

2) Diapering technique and toilet use, if care is provided to children in diapers and/or children needing help with toilet use, including appropriate diaper disposal and diaper-changing techniques. See Toilet, Diapering, and Bath Areas, STANDARD 5.116 through STANDARD 5.125; Toilet Use, Diapering, and Toilet Learning/ Training, STANDARD 3.012 through STANDARD 3.019; Toilet Learning/Training Equipment, Toilets, and Bathrooms, STANDARD 3.029 through STANDARD 3.033;

3) Identifying hazards and injury prevention;

4) Correct food preparation, serving, and storage techniques if employee prepares food. See Food Safety, STANDARD 4.042 through STANDARD 4.060;

5) Knowledge of when to exclude children due to illness and the means of illness transmission;

6) Formula preparation, if formula is handled. See Plans and Policies for Food Handling, Feeding, and Nutrition, STANDARD 8.035

and STANDARD 8.036; and Nutrition for Infants, STANDARD 4.011 through STANDARD 4.021;

7) Standard precautions and other measures to prevent exposure to blood and other body fluids, as well as program policies and procedures in the event of exposure to blood/body fluid. See Prevention of Exposure to Body Fluids, STANDARD 3.026;

n) Recognizing symptoms of illness. See Daily Health Assessment, STANDARD 3.001 and STANDARD 3.002;

o) Teaching health promotion concepts to children and parents as part of the daily care provided to children. See Health Education for Children, STANDARD 2.060 through STANDARD 2.063;

p) Child abuse detection, prevention, and reporting. See Child Abuse and Neglect, STANDARD 3.053 through STANDARD 3.059;

q) Medication administration policies and practices;

r) Putting infants down to sleep positioned on their backs and on a firm surface to reduce the risk of Sudden Infant Death Syndrome (SIDS).

Caregivers shall also receive continuing education each year, as specified in Continuing Education, STANDARD 1.029 through STANDARD 1.036.

TYPE OF FACILITY: *Center; Large Family Child Care Home; Small Family Child Care Home*

# STANDARD 1.024
# ORIENTATION FOR CARE OF CHILDREN WITH SPECIAL HEALTH NEEDS

When a child care facility enrolls a child with special needs, the facility shall ensure that staff members have been oriented in understanding that child's special needs and ways of working with that child in a group setting.

Caregivers in small family child care homes, who care for a child with special needs, shall meet with the parents and a health care worker involved with the child (if the parent has provided prior, informed, written consent) about the child's special needs and how these needs may affect his/her developmental progression or play with other children.

In addition to Orientation Training, STANDARD 1.023, the staff in child care facilities shall have orientation training based on the special needs of children in their care. This training may include, but is not limited to, the following topics:

a) Positioning for feeding and handling techniques of children with physical disabilities;

Rationale, comments and references for each Standard are located in *Caring for Our Children, 2nd Edition* (http://nrc.uchsc.edu/CFOC/index.html)

b)   Proper use and care of the individual child's adaptive equipment, including how to recognize defective equipment and to notify parents that repairs are needed;
c)   How different disabilities affect the child's ability to participate in group activities;
d)   Methods of helping the child with special needs to participate in the facility's programs;
e)   Role modeling, peer socialization, and interaction;
f)   Behavior modification techniques, positive rewards for children, promotion of self-esteem, and other techniques for managing difficult behavior;
g)   Grouping of children by skill levels, taking into account the child's age and developmental level;
h)   Intervention for children with special health care problems;
i)   Communication needs.

TYPE OF FACILITY: *Center; Large Family Child Care Home; Small Family Child Care Home*

# STANDARD 1.026
# FIRST AID TRAINING FOR STAFF

The director of a center and a large family child care home and the caregiver in a small family child care home shall ensure that all staff members involved in providing direct care have training in pediatric first aid, including management of a blocked airway and rescue breathing, as specified in STANDARD 1.027.

At least one staff person who has successfully completed training in pediatric first aid, as specified in STANDARD 1.027, shall be in attendance at all times and in all places where children are in care. Instances in which at least one staff member shall be certified in CPR include when children are involved in swimming and wading and when at least one child is known to have a specific special health need as determined by that child's physician (such as cardiac arrhythmia) that makes the child more likely than a typical child to require cardiac resuscitation. In each case of a child with a special health need, the child care provider shall ask the child's physician whether caregivers with skills in the management of a blocked airway and rescue breathing will suffice, or whether caregivers require skills in cardiac resuscitation to meet the particular health needs of the child.

Records of successful completion of training in pediatric first aid, as specified in STANDARD 1.027, shall be maintained in the files of the facility.

TYPE OF FACILITY: *Center; Large Family Child Care Home; Small Family Child Care Home*

# STANDARD 1.027
# TOPICS COVERED IN FIRST AID TRAINING

Management of a blocked airway and rescue breathing comprise two of the core elements of pediatric first aid training. In addition, the course must present an overview of the Emergency Medical Services (EMS), accessing EMS, safety at the scene, and isolation of body substances, and the first aid instruction that is offered shall include, but not be limited to, recognition and first response of pediatric emergency management in a child care setting of the following situations:
a) Abrasions and lacerations;
b) Bleeding, including nosebleeds;
c) Burns;
d) Fainting;
e) Poisoning, including swallowed, contact, and inhaled;
f) Puncture wounds, including splinters;
g) Injuries, including insect, animal, and human bites;
h) Shock;
i) Convulsions or nonconvulsive seizures;
j) Musculoskeletal injury (such as sprains, fractures);
k) Dental and mouth injuries;
l) Head injuries;
m) Allergic reactions, including information about when auto-injected epinephrine (Epi-Pen™) might be required;
n) Eye injuries;
o) Loss of consciousness;
p) Electric shock;
q) Drowning;
r) Heat-related injuries, including heat exhaustion/heat stroke;
s) Cold injuries;
t) Moving and positioning injured/ill persons;
u) Management of a blocked airway and rescue breathing for infants and children with return demonstration by the learner;
v) Illness-related emergencies (such as stiff neck, inexplicable confusion, sudden onset of blood-red or purple rash, severe pain, temperature of 105 degrees F or higher, or looking/acting severely ill);
w) Standard Precautions;

x)  Organizing and implementing a plan to meet an emergency for any child with a special health care need;
y)  Addressing the needs of the other children in the group while managing emergencies in a child care setting.

TYPE OF FACILITY: *Center; Large Family Child Care Home; Small Family Child Care Home*

## STANDARD 1.028
## CPR TRAINING FOR SWIMMING AND WADING

Facilities that have a swimming pool or use a water-filled wading pool shall require that at least one staff member with current documentation of successful completion of training in infant and child (pediatric) CPR (Cardiopulmonary Resuscitation) shall be on duty at all times during business hours.

At least one of the caregivers, volunteers, or other adults who is counted in the child:staff ratio for wading and swimming shall have documentation of successful completion of training in basic water safety and infant and child CPR according to the criteria of the American Red Cross or the American Heart Association.

For small family child care homes, the person trained in water safety and CPR shall be the caregiver. Written verification of successful completion of CPR and lifesaving training, water safety instructions, and emergency procedures shall be kept on file.

TYPE OF FACILITY: *Center; Large Family Child Care Home; Small Family Child Care Home*

## STANDARD 1.029
## CONTINUING EDUCATION FOR DIRECTORS AND CAREGIVERS IN CENTERS AND LARGE FAMILY CHILD CARE HOMES

All directors and caregivers of centers and large family child care homes shall successfully complete at least 30 clock hours per year of continuing education in the first year of employment, 16 clock hours of which shall be in child development programming and 14 of which shall be in child health, safety, and staff health. In the second and each of the following years of employment at a facility, all directors and caregivers shall successfully complete at least 24 clock hours of continuing education based on individual competency needs and any special needs of the children in their care, 16 hours of which shall be in child development programming and 8 hours of which shall be in child health, safety, and staff health.

The effectiveness of training shall be assessed by change in performance following participation in training.

TYPE OF FACILITY: *Center; Large Family Child Care Home*

## STANDARD 1.030
## CONTINUING EDUCATION FOR SMALL FAMILY CHILD CARE HOME PROVIDERS

Small family child care home providers shall have at least 24 clock hours of continuing education in areas determined by self-assessment and, where possible, by a performance review of a skilled mentor or peer reviewer.

TYPE OF FACILITY: *Small Family Child Care Home*

## STANDARD 1.031
## TRAINING OF STAFF WHO HANDLE FOOD

All staff members with food handling responsibilities shall obtain training in food service. The director of a center or a large family child care home or the designated supervisor for food service shall obtain certification equivalent to the Food Service Manager's Protection (Sanitation) certificate.

TYPE OF FACILITY: *Center; Large Family Child Care Home; Small Family Child Care Home*

## STANDARD 1.032
## CHILD ABUSE EDUCATION

Caregivers shall use child abuse prevention education materials provided by the licensing agency, state and national organizations, or from other community agencies such as local branches of the National Committee to Prevent Child Abuse, to educate and establish child abuse prevention and recognition measures for the children, caregivers, and parents. The education and prevention shall address physical, sexual, and psychological or emotional abuse, injury prevention, the dangers of shaking infants and

Rationale, comments and references for each Standard are located in *Caring for Our Children, 2nd Edition* (http://nrc.uchsc.edu/CFOC/index.html)

toddlers, as well as signs and symptoms of sexually transmitted diseases. Child care directors and head teachers shall participate in training to recognize visible signs of child abuse, including pattern marks, bruises in unusual locations, pattern or immersion burns, shaken baby syndrome, and behaviors suggesting sexual abuse. They shall know how to refer children with vaginal, penile, or rectal discharge or bleeding to their health provider. A child care provider shall refer the child to the local child protection agency for any reasonable suspicion of child abuse or neglect.

Caregivers shall be trained in compliance with their state's child abuse reporting laws.

TYPE OF FACILITY: *Center; Large Family Child Care Home; Small Family Child Care Home*

## STANDARD 1.033
## TRAINING ON OCCUPATIONAL RISK RELATED TO HANDLING BODY FLUIDS

The director of a center or a large family child care home caregiver shall ensure that all staff members who are at risk of occupational exposure to blood or other blood-containing body fluids will be offered hepatitis B immunizations and will receive annual training in Standard Precautions. Training shall be consistent with applicable standards of the Occupational Safety and Health Administration (OSHA Standard 29 CFR 1910.1030, "Occupational Exposure to Bloodborne Pathogens") and local occupational health requirements and shall include, but not be limited to:
a) Modes of transmission of bloodborne pathogens;
b) Standard Precautions;
c) Hepatitis B vaccine, pre-exposure, or post-exposure within 24 hours;
d) Program policies and procedures regarding exposure to blood/body fluid;
e) Reporting procedures under the exposure control plan to ensure that all first-aid incidents involving exposure are reported to the employer before the end of the work shift during which the incident occurs.

TYPE OF FACILITY: *Center; Large Family Child Care Home*

## STANDARD 1.037
## EMPLOYMENT OF SUBSTITUTES

Substitutes shall be employed to ensure that child:staff ratios (as specified in Child:Staff Ratio and Group Size, STANDARD 1.001 through STANDARD 1.005) are maintained at all times. Substitutes and volunteers must meet the requirements specified in General Qualifications for All Caregivers, STANDARD 1.007 through STANDARD 1.013. Those without licenses/certificates shall work under direct supervision and shall not be alone with a group of children.

A substitute shall have the same clearances as the provider including criminal record check, child abuse history, and medical assessment.

TYPE OF FACILITY: *Center; Large Family Child Care Home*

## STANDARD 1.039
## ORIENTATION FOR SUBSTITUTES FOR SMALL FAMILY CHILD CARE HOMES

A short-term substitute caregiver in a small family child care home shall be oriented on the first day of employment to emergency response practices, including how to call for emergency medical assistance, how to reach parents or emergency contacts, how to arrange for transfer to medical care, and the evacuation plan.

TYPE OF FACILITY: *Small Family Child Care Home*

## STANDARD 1.040
## USE OF CHILD CARE HEALTH CONSULTANTS

Each center, large family child care home, and small family child care home network shall use the services of a health consultant qualified to provide advice for child care as defined in STANDARD 1.041. Centers and large and small family child care home providers shall avail themselves of community resources established for health consultation to child care.

TYPE OF FACILITY: *Center; Large Family Child Care Home; Small Family Child Care Home*

Rationale, comments and references for each Standard are located in *Caring for Our Children, 2nd Edition* (http://nrc.uchsc.edu/CFOC/index.html)

# STANDARD 1.041
## KNOWLEDGE AND SKILLS OF CHILD CARE HEALTH CONSULTANTS

A facility shall have a health consultant who is a health professional with training and experience as a child care health consultant. Graduate students in a discipline related to child health shall be acceptable as child care health consultants supervised by faculty knowledgeable in child care. A child care health consultant shall either have the full knowledge base and skills required for this role, or arrange to partner with other health professionals who can provide the necessary knowledge and skills.

The knowledge base of the child care health consultant (personally or by involving other health professionals) shall include:
a)   National health and safety standards for out-of-home child care;
b)   How child care facilities conduct their day-to-day operations;
c)   Child care licensing requirements;
d)   Disease reporting requirements for child care providers;
e)   Immunizations for children;
f)   Immunizations for child care providers;
g)   Injury prevention for children;
h)   Staff health, including occupational health risks for child care providers;
i)   Oral health for children;
j)   Nutrition for children;
k)   Inclusion of children with special health needs in child care;
l)   Recognition and reporting requirements for child abuse and neglect;
m)   Community health and mental health resources for child and parent health.

The skills of the child care health consultant shall include the ability to perform or arrange for performance of the following activities:
a)   Teaching child care providers about health and safety issues;
b)   Teaching parents about health and safety issues;
c)   Assessing child care providers' needs for health and safety training;
d)   Assessing parents' needs for health and safety training;
e)   Meeting on-site with child care providers about health and safety;
f)   Providing telephone advice to child care providers about health and safety;
g)   Providing referrals to community services;
h)   Developing or updating policies and procedures for child care facilities;
i)   Reviewing health records of children;
j)   Reviewing health records of child care providers;
k)   Helping to manage the care of children with special health care needs;
l)   Consulting with a child's health professional about medication;

m) Interpreting standards or regulations and providing technical advice, separate and apart from the enforcement role of a regulation inspector.

Although the child care health consultant may have a dual role, such as providing direct care to some of the children or serving as a regulation inspector, these roles shall not be mixed with the child care health consultation role.

The child care health consultant shall have contact with the facility's administrative authority, the staff, and the parents in the facility. The administrative authority shall review, respond to, and implement the child care health consultant's recommendations. The child care health consultant shall review and approve the written health policies used by center-based facilities.

Programs with a significant number of non-English-speaking families shall seek a child care health consultant who is culturally sensitive and knowledgeable about community health resources for the parents' native culture and languages.

TYPE OF FACILITY: *Center; Large Family Child Care Home; Small Family Child Care Home*

## STANDARD 1.043
## FREQUENCY OF CHILD CARE HEALTH CONSULTATION VISITS

The health consultant shall visit each facility as needed to review and give advice on the facility's health component. Center-based facilities that serve any child younger than 2 years of age shall be visited at least once a month by a health professional with general knowledge and skills in child health and safety. Center-based facilities that are not open at least 5 days a week or that serve only children 2 years of age or older shall be visited at least quarterly, on a schedule that meets the needs of the composite group of children. Small and large family child care homes shall be visited at least annually. Written documentation of health consultant visits shall be maintained at the facility.

TYPE OF FACILITY: *Center; Large Family Child Care Home; Small Family Child Care Home*

Rationale, comments and references for each Standard are located in *Caring for Our Children, 2nd Edition* (http://nrc.uchsc.edu/CFOC/index.html)

# STANDARD 1.045
# PREEMPLOYMENT AND ONGOING ADULT HEALTH APPRAISALS, INCLUDING IMMUNIZATION

All paid and volunteer staff members who work more than 40 hours per month shall have a health appraisal before their first involvement in child care work. Health appraisals shall be required every 2 years thereafter, unless the staff member's health provider recommends that this be done more frequently. If a child care provider works also at a different child care facility, a new health appraisal shall be required if there is a question about the results of the previous health appraisal, 2 years have elapsed since the previous health appraisal, or signs of ill health appear. People who work less than 40 hours per month shall be encouraged to have a health appraisal. The appraisal shall identify any accommodations required of the facility for the staff person to function in his or her assigned position. A statement from the health care provider that an appraisal covering the listed areas was completed, and details about any findings that require accommodation shall be on file at the facility.

Health appraisals for paid and volunteer staff members who work more than 40 hours per month shall include at a minimum:
a)  Health history;
b)  Physical exam;
c)  Dental exam;
d)  Vision and hearing screening;
e)  The results and appropriate follow-up of a tuberculosis (Tb) screening using the Mantoux intradermal skin test, one-step procedure. See STANDARD 6.014;
f)  A review and certification of up-to-date immune status (measles, mumps, rubella, diphtheria, tetanus, polio, varicella, influenza, pneumonia, hepatitis A, and hepatitis B). See Immunizations, STANDARD 3.005 through STANDARD 3.007;
g)  A review of occupational health concerns based on the performance of the essential functions of the job. See Occupational Hazards, STANDARD 1.048; and *Major Occupational Health Hazards*, Appendix B;
h)  Assessment of risk from exposure to common childhood infections, such as parvovirus, CMV, and chickenpox;
i)  Assessment of orthopedic, psychological, neurological, or sensory limitations or communicable diseases that require accommodations or modifications for the person to perform tasks that typical adults can do.

All adults who reside in a family child care home who are considered to be at high risk for Tb, and all adults who work less than 40 hours in any month in child care shall have completed Tb screening as specified in STANDARD 6.014. Adults who are considered at high risk for Tb include those who are foreign-born, have a history of homelessness, are HIV-infected, have contact with a prison population, or have contact with someone who has active Tb.

The Tb test of staff members with previously negative skin tests shall not be repeated on a regular basis unless required by the local or state health department. A record of test results and appropriate follow-up evaluation shall be on file in the facility.

All adults who work in child care shall be encouraged to have a full health appraisal.

TYPE OF FACILITY: *Center; Large Family Child Care Home; Small Family Child Care Home*

# STANDARD 1.046
## DAILY STAFF HEALTH ASSESSMENT

On a daily basis, the administrator of the facility or caregiver shall assess (visually and verbally) staff members, substitutes, and volunteers for obvious signs of ill health. Staff members, substitutes, and volunteers shall be responsible for reporting immediately to their supervisor any injuries or illnesses they experience at the facility or elsewhere, especially those that might affect their health or the health and safety of the children. It is the responsibility of the administration, not the ill or injured staff member, to arrange for a substitute provider.

TYPE OF FACILITY: *Center; Large Family Child Care Home; Small Family Child Care Home*

# STANDARD 1.048
## OCCUPATIONAL HAZARDS

The center's written personnel policies shall address the major occupational health hazards for workers in child care settings. Special health concerns of pregnant providers shall be carefully evaluated, and up-to-date information regarding occupational hazards for pregnant providers shall be made available to them and other workers. The occupational hazards including those regarding pregnant workers listed in Appendix B (*Major Occupational Health Hazards*) shall be referenced and used in evaluations by providers and supervisors.

TYPE OF FACILITY: *Center; Large Family Child Care Home*

# CHAPTER 2 - PROGRAM: ACTIVITIES FOR HEALTHY DEVELOPMENT

## STANDARD 2.006
## COMMUNICATION IN NATIVE LANGUAGE

At least one member of the staff shall be able to communicate in the native language of the parents and children, or the facility shall work with parents to arrange for a translator to communicate with parents and children.

TYPE OF FACILITY: *Center; Large Family Child Care Home; Small Family Child Care Home*

## STANDARD 2.009
## PLAYING OUTDOORS

Children shall play outdoors daily when weather and air quality conditions do not pose a significant health risk. Outdoor play for infants may include riding in a carriage or stroller; however, infants shall be offered opportunities for gross motor play outdoors, as well.

Weather that poses a significant health risk shall include wind chill at or below 15 degrees F and heat index at or above 90 degrees F, as identified by the National Weather Service.

Air quality conditions that pose a significant health risk shall be identified by announcements from local health authorities or through ozone (smog) alerts. Such air quality conditions shall require that children remain indoors where air conditioners ventilate indoor air to the outdoors. Children with respiratory health problems such as asthma shall not play outdoors when local health authorities announce that the air quality is approaching unhealthy levels.

Children shall be protected from the sun by using shade, sun-protective clothing, and sunscreen with UVB-ray and UVA-ray protection of SPF-15 or higher, with permission as described in STANDARD 3.081, during outdoor play. Before prolonged physical activity in warm weather, children shall be well-hydrated and shall be encouraged to drink water during the activity. In warm weather, children's clothing shall be light-colored, lightweight, and limited to one layer of absorbent material to facilitate the evaporation of sweat. Children shall wear sun-protective clothing, such as hats, long-sleeved shirts and pants, when playing outdoors between the hours of 10 AM and 2 PM.

In cold weather, children's clothing shall be layered and dry. Caregivers shall check children's extremities for maintenance of normal color and warmth at least every 15 minutes when children are outdoors in cold weather.

TYPE OF FACILITY: *Center; Large Family Child Care Home; Small Family Child Care Home*

## STANDARD 2.010
## PERSONAL CAREGIVER RELATIONSHIPS FOR INFANTS AND TODDLERS

Opportunities shall be provided for each child to develop a personal and affectionate relationship with, and attachment to, that child's parents and one or a small number of caregivers whose care for and responsiveness to the child ensure relief of distress, experiences of comfort and stimulation, and satisfaction of the need for a personal relationship. The facility shall limit the number of caregivers who interact with any one infant to no more than three caregivers in a given day and no more than five caregivers across the period that the child is an infant in child care. The caregivers shall:
a)   Hold and comfort children who are upset;
b)   Engage in social interchanges such as smiling, talking, touching, singing, and eating;
c)   Be play partners as well as protectors;
d)   Attune to children's feelings and reflect them back.

TYPE OF FACILITY: *Center; Large Family Child Care Home; Small Family Child Care Home*

## STANDARD 2.011
## INTERACTIONS WITH INFANTS AND TODDLERS

Caregivers shall talk, listen to, and otherwise interact with young infants as they feed, change, and cuddle them.

TYPE OF FACILITY: *Center; Large Family Child Care Home; Small Family Child Care Home*

## STANDARD 2.012
## SPACE AND ACTIVITY TO SUPPORT LEARNING OF INFANTS AND TODDLERS

The facility shall provide a safe and clean space, both indoors and outdoors, and colorful material and equipment arranged to support learning. The facility shall provide opportunities for the child to act upon the environment by experiencing age-appropriate obstacles, frustrations, and risks in order to learn to manage inner feelings and resources, as well as the occurrences and demands of the outer world. The facility shall provide opportunities for play that:

- Lessen the child's anxiety and help the child adapt to reality and resolve conflicts;
- Enable the child to explore the real world;
- Help the child practice resolving conflicts;
- Use symbols (words, numbers, and letters);
- Manipulate objects;
- Exercise physical skills;
- Encourage language development;
- Foster self-expression;
- Strengthen the child's identity as a member of a family and a cultural community.

TYPE OF FACILITY: *Center; Large Family Child Care Home; Small Family Child Care Home*

## STANDARD 2.014
## PERSONAL CAREGIVER RELATIONSHIPS FOR 3- TO 5-YEAR-OLDS

Facilities shall provide opportunities for each child to build long-term, trusting relationships with a few caring caregivers by limiting the number of adults the facility permits to care for any one child in child care to a maximum of 8 adults in a given year and no more than 3 in a day.

TYPE OF FACILITY: *Center; Large Family Child Care Home; Small Family Child Care Home*

## STANDARD 2.015
## OPPORTUNITIES FOR LEARNING FOR 3- TO 5-YEAR-OLDS

Facilities shall provide opportunities for children to observe, explore, order and reorder, make mistakes and find solutions, and move from the concrete to the abstract in learning.

TYPE OF FACILITY: *Center; Large Family Child Care Home; Small Family Child Care Home*

## STANDARD 2.018
## FOSTERING COOPERATION OF 3- TO 5-YEAR-OLDS

Facilities shall foster a cooperative rather than a competitive atmosphere.

TYPE OF FACILITY: *Center; Large Family Child Care Home; Small Family Child Care Home*

## STANDARD 2.028
## METHODS OF SUPERVISION

Caregivers shall directly supervise infants, toddlers, and preschool children by sight and hearing at all times, even when the children are in sleeping areas. Caregivers shall not be on one floor level of the building, while children are on another floor.

School-age children shall be permitted to participate in activities off the premises with written approval by a parent and by the caregiver.

Caregivers shall regularly count children on a scheduled basis, at every transition, and whenever leaving one area and arriving at another, to confirm the safe whereabouts of every child at all times.

Developmentally appropriate child:staff ratios shall be met during all hours of operation, including indoor and outdoor play and field trips, following precautions for specific areas and equipment. No center-based facility shall operate with fewer than two staff members if more than six children are in care, even if the group otherwise meets the child:staff ratio. Although centers often downsize the number of staff for the early arrival and late departure times, another adult must be present to help in

Rationale, comments and references for each Standard are located in *Caring for Our Children, 2nd Edition* (http://nrc.uchsc.edu/CFOC/index.html)

the event of an emergency. The supervision policies of centers and large family child care homes shall be written policies.

*Editor's Note: This standard also applies to outdoor activities.*

TYPE OF FACILITY: *Center; Large Family Child Care Home; Small Family Child Care Home*

## STANDARD 2.029
## COMPETENCE AND TRAINING OF
## TRANSPORTATION STAFF

At least one adult who accompanies or drives children for field trips and out-of-facility activities shall receive training by a professional knowledgeable about child development and procedures to ensure the safety of all children. The caregiver shall hold a valid pediatric first aid certificate, including rescue breathing and management of blocked airways, as specified in First Aid and CPR, STANDARD 1.026 through STANDARD 1.028.

All drivers, passenger monitors, chaperones, and assistants shall receive instructions in safety precautions. If transportation is provided, these instructions shall include:
a) Use of developmentally appropriate safety restraints;
b) Proper placement of the child in the motor vehicle;
c) Handling of emergency situations. If a child has a chronic medical condition that could result in an emergency (such as asthma, diabetes, seizures), the driver or chaperone shall have written instructions including parent emergency contacts, child summary health information, special needs, and treatment plans, and shall be trained to;
   1) Recognize the signs of a medical emergency;
   2) Know emergency procedures to follow;
   3) Have on-hand, any emergency supplies or medications necessary;
d) Map and appropriate route to emergency facility;
e) Defensive driving;
f) Child supervision during transport, including never leaving a child unattended in a vehicle.

The receipt of such instructions shall be documented in a personnel record for any paid staff or volunteer who participates in field trips or transportation activities. Child:staff ratios shall be maintained on field trips and during transport, as specified in STANDARD 1.001 through STANDARD 1.005.

TYPE OF FACILITY: *Center; Large Family Child Care Home; Small Family Child Care Home*

## STANDARD 2.030
## QUALIFICATIONS FOR DRIVERS

Any driver who transports children for a child care program shall be at least 21 years of age and shall have:
a) A valid driver's license that authorizes the driver to operate the vehicle being driven;
b) Evidence of a safe driving record for more than five years, with no crashes where a citation was issued;
c) No record of substance abuse or conviction for crimes of violence or child abuse;
d) No alcohol or other drugs associated with impaired ability to drive within 12 hours prior to transporting children. Drivers shall ensure that any prescription drugs taken will not impair their ability to drive;
e) No criminal record of crimes against or involving children, child neglect or abuse, or any crime of violence.

The driver's license number, vehicle insurance information, and verification of current state vehicle inspection shall be on file in the facility.

The center director shall require drug testing when noncompliance with the restriction on the use of alcohol or other drugs is suspected.

TYPE OF FACILITY: *Center; Large Family Child Care Home; Small Family Child Care Home*

## STANDARD 2.033
## VEHICLE SAFETY RESTRAINTS

When children are driven in a motor vehicle other than a bus, school bus, or a bus operated by a common carrier, the following shall apply:
• A child shall be transported only if the child is fastened in an approved developmentally appropriate safety seat, seat belt, or harness appropriate to the child's weight, and the restraint is installed and used in accordance with the manufacturers' instructions

for the car seat and the motor vehicle. Each child must have an individual seat belt and be positioned in the vehicle in accordance with the requirements for the safe use of air bags in the back seat;

- A child under the age of 4 shall be transported only if the child is securely fastened in a developmentally appropriate child passenger restraint system that meets the federal motor vehicle safety standards contained in the Code of Federal Regulations, Title 49, Section 571.213, and this compliance is so indicated on the safety restraint device;
- If small buses or vans have safety restraints installed, children weighing over 40 pounds shall have access to belt-positioning booster seats with lap and shoulder belts. Children weighing under 40 pounds shall use car safety seats;
- Vehicles shall accommodate the placement of wheelchairs with four tie-downs affixed according to the manufactures' instructions in a forward-facing direction. The wheelchair occupant shall be secured by a three-point tie restraint during transport.

TYPE OF FACILITY: *Center; Large Family Child Care Home; Small Family Child Care Home*

# STANDARD 2.038
# EMERGENCY SUPPLIES FOR FIELD TRIPS

First aid kits shall be taken on field trips, as specified in STANDARD 5.093. Cellular phones shall be taken on field trips for use in emergency situations.

TYPE OF FACILITY: *Center; Large Family Child Care Home; Small Family Child Care Home*

# STANDARD 2.039
# DISCIPLINE MEASURES

Discipline shall include positive guidance, re-direction, and setting clear-cut limits that foster the child's ability to become self-disciplined. Disciplinary measures shall be clear and understandable to the child, shall be consistent, and shall be explained to the child before and at the time of any disciplinary action.

Caregivers shall guide children to develop self control and orderly conduct in relationships with peers and adults. Caregivers shall show children positive alternatives rather than just telling children "no."

Caregivers shall care for children without resorting to physical punishment or abusive language. Caregivers shall acknowledge and model desired behavior.

For children 3 or over, facilities shall selectively use "time out" only to enable the child to regain control of himself or herself. The caregiver shall keep the child within visual contact. The caregiver shall take into account the child's developmental stage, tolerances, and ability to learn from "time out."

Expectations for children's behavior shall be written and shared with families and children of appropriate age.

TYPE OF FACILITY: *Center; Large Family Child Care Home; Small Family Child Care Home*

# STANDARD 2.042
# PROHIBITED CAREGIVER BEHAVIORS

The following behaviors shall be prohibited in all child care settings and by all caregivers:
a) Corporal punishment, including beating, hitting, spanking, shaking, pinching, excessive exercise, exposure to extreme temperatures, and other measures producing physical pain;
b) Withdrawal or the threat of withdrawal of food, or forcing of food, rest, or bathroom opportunities;
c) Abusive or profane language or verbal abuse, threats, or derogatory remarks about the child or child's family;
d) Any form of public or private humiliation, including threats of physical punishment;
e) Any form of emotional abuse, including rejecting, terrorizing, ignoring, isolating, or corrupting a child;
f) Binding or tying to restrict movement, such as in a car seat (except when travelling); or enclosing in a confined space such as a closet, locked room, box, or similar cubicle.

TYPE OF FACILITY: *Center; Large Family Child Care Home; Small Family Child Care Home*

Rationale, comments and references for each Standard are located in *Caring for Our Children, 2nd Edition* (http://nrc.uchsc.edu/CFOC/index.html)

## STANDARD 2.043
## USING PHYSICAL RESTRAINT

When a child's behavior makes it necessary, for his own or others' protection, to restrain the child, the most desirable method of restraint is holding the child by another person as gently as possible to accomplish the restraint. Children shall not be physically restrained longer than necessary to control the situation. No bonds, ties, or straps shall be employed to restrain young children.

Children shall not be given medicines, drugs, or herbal or folk remedies that will affect their behavior except as prescribed by their health care provider and with specific written instructions from their health care provider for use of the medicine.

The decision to restrain the child shall be made by the staff person with the most experience in child care and shall only be made for extreme circumstances. Training in the use of any form of physical restraint shall be provided by persons with extensive child care experience including experience with children who have required restraint.

TYPE OF FACILITY: *Center; Large Family Child Care Home; Small Family Child Care Home*

## STANDARD 2.044
## MUTUAL RESPONSIBILITY OF PARENTS AND STAFF

There shall be a reciprocal responsibility of the family and child care staff to observe, participate, and be trained in the care that each child requires.

All aspects of child care programs shall be designed to facilitate parental input and involvement. Involved, non-custodial parents shall have access to the same developmental and behavioral information given to the custodial parent, if they have joint legal custody, permission by court order, or written consent from the custodial parent.

Caregivers shall informally share with parents daily information about their child's needs and activities.

TYPE OF FACILITY: *Center; Large Family Child Care Home; Small Family Child Care Home*

## STANDARD 2.046
## PARENT VISITS

Caregivers shall inform all parents that they may visit the site at any time when their child is there, and that, under normal circumstances, they will be admitted without delay. This open-door policy shall be part of the "admission agreement" or other contract between the parent and the caregiver, if they have custody, joint custody, permission by court order, or written consent from the custodial parent. Parents are welcomed and encouraged to speak freely to staff about concerns and suggestions.

TYPE OF FACILITY: *Center; Large Family Child Care Home; Small Family Child Care Home*

## STANDARD 2.047
## PARENT CONFERENCES

Along with short informal daily conversations between parents and caregivers, planned communication (for example, parent conferences) shall be scheduled with at least one parent of every child in care:
a)   To review the child's development and adjustment to care;
b)   To reach agreement on appropriate, nonviolent, disciplinary measures;
c)   To discuss the child's strengths, specific health issues, and concerns such as persistent behavior problems, developmental delays, special needs, overweight, underweight, or eating or sleeping problems.

At these planned conferences a caregiver shall review with the parent the child's health report and the health record to identify medical and developmental issues that require follow-up or adjustment of the facility.

Each review shall be documented in the child's facility health record with the signature of the parent and the staff reviewer. These planned conferences shall occur:
a)   As part of the intake process;
b)   At each health update interval;
c)   On a calendar basis, scheduled according to the child's age:
   1)   Every 6 months for children under 6 years of age;
   2)   Every year for children 6 years of age and older;
d)   Whenever new information is added to the child's facility health record.

Additional conferences shall be scheduled if the parent or caregiver has a concern at any time about a particular child. Any concern about a child's health or development shall not be delayed until a scheduled conference date.

Notes about these planned communications shall be maintained in each child's record at the facility and shall be available for review.

TYPE OF FACILITY: *Center; Large Family Child Care Home; Small Family Child Care Home*

## STANDARD 2.054
## PARENTS' INFORMATION ON THEIR CHILD'S HEALTH AND BEHAVIOR

The facility shall ask parents for information regarding the child's health and behavioral status upon registration or if there has been an extended gap in the child's attendance at the facility.

TYPE OF FACILITY: *Center; Large Family Child Care Home; Small Family Child Care Home*

# CHAPTER 3 - HEALTH PROMOTION AND PROTECTION IN CHILD CARE

## STANDARD 3.001
## CONDUCT OF DAILY HEALTH CHECK

Every day, a trained staff member shall conduct a health check of each child. This health check shall be conducted as soon as possible after the child enters the child care facility and whenever a change occurs while that child is in care. The health check shall address:
a) Changes in behavior (such as lethargy or drowsiness) or appearance from behaviors observed during the previous day's attendance;
b) Skin rashes, itchy skin, itchy scalp, or (during a lice outbreak) nits;
c) If there is a change in the child's behavior or appearance, elevated body temperature, determined by taking the child's temperature;
d) Complaints of pain or of not feeling well;
e) Other signs or symptoms of illness (such as drainage from eyes, vomiting, diarrhea, and so on);

f) Reported illness or injury in child or family members since last date of attendance.

The facility shall gain information necessary to complete the daily health check by direct observation of the child, by querying the parent or legal guardian, and, where applicable, by conversation with the child.

TYPE OF FACILITY: *Center; Large Family Child Care Home; Small Family Child Care Home*

## STANDARD 3.006
## UNDER-IMMUNIZED CHILDREN

If immunizations are not to be administered because of a medical condition, a statement from the child's health care provider documenting the reason why the child is exempt from the immunization requirement shall be on file.

If immunizations are not given because of parents' religious beliefs, a waiver signed by the parent shall be on file. If a child who is not immunized is in care, the parents must be notified of the risk of the spread of preventable diseases.

Children who have not received their age-appropriate immunizations prior to enrollment and do not have documented religious or medical exemptions from routine childhood immunizations shall show evidence of an appointment for immunizations. The immunization series shall be initiated within one month and completed according to the *Recommended Childhood Immunization Schedule* from the American Academy of Pediatrics (AAP). See Appendix G.

If a vaccine-preventable disease to which children are susceptible occurs in the facility, unimmunized children shall be excluded for the duration of possible exposure or until the age-appropriate immunizations have been completed (whichever comes first).

TYPE OF FACILITY: *Center; Large Family Child Care Home; Small Family Child Care Home*

## STANDARD 3.008
## SCHEDULED REST PERIODS AND SLEEP ARRANGEMENTS

The facility shall provide an opportunity for, but shall not require, sleep and rest. The facility shall make available a regular rest period for school-aged children, if the child desires. For children who are unable to sleep, the facility shall provide time and space for quiet play.

Unless the child has a note from a physician specifying otherwise, infants shall be placed in a supine (back) position for sleeping to lower the risks of Sudden Infant Death Syndrome (SIDS). Soft surfaces and gas-trapping objects such as pillows, quilts, sheepskins, soft bumpers or waterbeds shall not be placed under or with an infant for sleeping. When infants can easily turn over from the supine to the prone position, they shall be put down to sleep on their back, but allowed to adopt whatever position they prefer for sleep.

Unless a doctor specifies the need for a positioning device that restricts movement within the child's bed, such devices shall not be used.

TYPE OF FACILITY: *Center; Large Family Child Care Home; Small Family Child Care Home*

## STANDARD 3.010
## ROUTINE ORAL HYGIENE ACTIVITIES

Caregivers shall promote the habit of regular tooth brushing. All children with teeth shall brush or have their teeth brushed at least once during the hours the child is in child care. Using a size-appropriate brush and a small amount of fluoride toothpaste, the caregiver shall either brush the child's teeth or supervise as the child brushes his/her own teeth. The younger the child the more the caregiver needs to be involved. After feeding, an infant's teeth and gums shall be wiped with a moist cloth to remove any remaining liquid that coats the teeth and gums and which turns to plaque causing tooth decay. Very few preschool-age children have the hand-eye coordination or the fine motor skills necessary to complete the complex process of tooth brushing. The caregiver shall be able to evaluate each child's motor activity and to teach the child the correct method of tooth brushing when the child is capable of doing this activity. The caregiver shall monitor the tooth brushing activity and thoroughly brush the child's teeth after the child has finished brushing.

The cavity-causing effect of frequent exposure to food shall be reduced by offering the children rinsing water after snacks when brushing is not possible.

*Editor's Note: The rationale and comment sections of this standard indicate that a small amount equals "pea size" amount.*

TYPE OF FACILITY: *Center; Large Family Child Care Home; Small Family Child Care Home*

## STANDARD 3.011
## ORAL HEALTH EDUCATION

All children with teeth shall have oral hygiene as a part of their daily activity. Those two years and older shall have developmentally appropriate oral health education that includes information on what plaque is, the process of dental caries development, and the importance of good oral hygiene behaviors. School-age children shall receive additional information including the preventive use of fluoride, dental sealants, mouth guards, and the importance of healthy eating behaviors and regularly scheduled dental visits. Older children shall be informed about the effect of tobacco products on their oral health and additional reasons for avoidance.

TYPE OF FACILITY: *Center*

## STANDARD 3.012
## TYPE OF DIAPERS

Diapers worn by children shall be able to contain urine and stool and minimize fecal contamination of the children, caregivers, environmental surfaces, and objects in the child care setting. Only disposable diapers with absorbent gelling material or carboxymethyl cellulose may be used unless the child has a medical reason that does not permit the use of disposable diapers (such as allergic reactions). When children cannot use disposable diapers for a medical reason, the reason shall be documented by the child's health care provider.

When cloth diapers are used, the diaper shall have an absorbent inner lining completely contained within an outer covering made of waterproof material that prevents the escape of feces and urine. The outer covering and inner lining shall be changed together at the same time as a unit and shall not be reused unless both are cleaned and disinfected, washed, and either chemically disinfected or heat dried at 165 degrees F or more. No rinsing or dumping of the contents of the diaper shall be performed at the child care facility.

TYPE OF FACILITY: *Center; Large Family Child Care Home; Small Family Child Care Home*

## STANDARD 3.014
## DIAPER CHANGE PROCEDURE

The following diaper changing procedure shall be posted in the changing area, shall be followed for all diaper changes, and shall be used as part of staff evaluation of caregivers who do diaper changing. Child caregivers shall never leave a child alone on a table or countertop, even for an instant. A safety strap or harness shall not be used on the diaper changing table. If an emergency arises, caregivers shall put the child on the floor or take the child with them.

Step 1: Get organized. Before you bring the child to the diaper changing area, wash your hands, gather and bring what you need to the diaper changing table:
* Non-absorbent paper liner large enough to cover the changing surface from the child's shoulders to beyond the child's feet;
* Fresh diaper, clean clothes (if you need them);
* Wipes for cleaning the child's genitalia and buttocks removed from the container or dispensed so the container will not be touched during diaper changing;
* A plastic bag for any soiled clothes;
* Disposable gloves, if you plan to use them (put gloves on before handling soiled clothing or diapers);
* A thick application of any diaper cream (when appropriate) removed from the container to a piece of disposable material such as facial or toilet tissue.

Step 2: Carry the child to the changing table, keeping soiled clothing away from you and any surfaces you cannot easily clean and sanitize after the change.
* Always keep a hand on the child;
* If the child's feet cannot be kept out of the diaper or from contact with soiled skin during the changing process, remove the child's shoes and socks so the child does not contaminate these surfaces with stool or urine during the diaper changing;
* Put soiled clothes in a plastic bag and securely tie the plastic bag to send the soiled clothes home.

Step 3: Clean the child's diaper area.
* Place the child on the diaper change surface and unfasten the diaper but leave the soiled diaper under the child.
* If safety pins are used, close each pin immediately once it is removed and keep pins out of the child's reach. Never hold pins in your mouth.
* Lift the child's legs as needed to use disposable wipes to clean the skin on the child's genitalia and buttocks. Remove stool and urine from front to back and use a fresh wipe each time. Put the soiled wipes into the soiled diaper or directly into a plastic-lined, hands-free covered can.

Step 4: Remove the soiled diaper without contaminating any surface not already in contact with stool or urine.
* Fold the soiled surface of the diaper inward.
* Put soiled disposable diapers in a covered, plastic-lined, hands-free covered can. If reusable cloth diapers are used, put the soiled cloth diaper and its contents (without emptying or rinsing) in a plastic bag or into a plastic-lined, hands-free covered can to give to parents or laundry service.
* If gloves were used, remove them using the proper technique (see Appendix D) and put them into a plastic-lined, hands-free covered can.
* Whether or not gloves were used, use a disposable wipe to clean the surfaces of the caregiver's hands and another to clean the child's hands, and put the wipes into the plastic-lined, hands-free covered can.
* Check for spills under the child. If there are any, use the paper that extends under the child's feet to fold over the disposable paper so a fresh, unsoiled paper surface is now under the child's buttocks.

Step 5: Put on a clean diaper and dress the child.
* Slide a fresh diaper under the child.
* Use a facial or toilet tissue to apply any necessary diaper creams, discarding the tissue in a covered, plastic-lined, hands-free covered can.
* Note and plan to report any skin problems such as redness, skin cracks, or bleeding.
* Fasten the diaper. If pins are used, place your hand between the child and the diaper when inserting the pin.

Step 6: Wash the child's hands and return the child to a supervised area.
* Use soap and water, no less than 60 degrees F and no more than 120 degrees F, at a sink to wash the child's hands, if you can.
* If a child is too heavy to hold for handwashing or cannot stand at the sink, use commercial disposable diaper wipes or follow this procedure:

Rationale, comments and references for each Standard are located in *Caring for Our Children, 2nd Edition* (http://nrc.uchsc.edu/CFOC/index.html)

- Wipe the child's hands with a damp paper towel moistened with a drop of liquid soap.
- Wipe the child's hands with a paper towel wet with clear water.
- Dry the child's hands with a paper towel.

Step 7: Clean and sanitize the diaper-changing surface.
- Dispose of the disposable paper liner used on the diaper changing surface in a plastic-lined, hands-free covered can.
- Clean any visible soil from the changing surface with detergent and water; rinse with water.
- Wet the entire changing surface with the sanitizing solution (e.g. spray a sanitizing bleach solution of 1/4 cup of household liquid chlorine bleach in one gallon of tap water, mixed fresh daily).
- Put away the spray bottle of sanitizer. If the recommended bleach dilution is sprayed as a sanitizer on the surface, leave it in contact with the surface for at least 2 minutes. The surface can be left to air dry or can be wiped dry after 2 minutes of contact with the bleach solution.

Step 8: Wash your hands according to the procedure in STANDARD 3.021 and record the diaper change in the child's daily log.
- In the daily log, record what was in the diaper and any problems (such as a loose stool, an unusual odor, blood in the stool, or any skin irritation). Report as necessary.

TYPE OF FACILITY: *Center; Large Family Child Care Home; Small Family Child Care Home*

## STANDARD 3.020
## SITUATIONS THAT REQUIRE HANDWASHING

All staff, volunteers, and children shall follow the procedure in STANDARD 3.021 for handwashing at the following times:
a)  Upon arrival for the day or when moving from one child care group to another;
b)  Before and after:
    - Eating, handling food, or feeding a child;
    - Giving medication;
    - Playing in water that is used by more than one person.
c)  After:
    - Diapering;
    - Using the toilet or helping a child use a toilet;
    - Handling bodily fluid (mucus, blood, vomit), from sneezing, wiping and blowing noses, from mouths, or from sores;
    - Handling uncoooked food, especially raw meat and poultry;

- Handling pets and other animals;
- Playing in sandboxes;
- Cleaning or handling the garbage.

TYPE OF FACILITY: *Center; Large Family Child Care Home; Small Family Child Care Home*

## STANDARD 3.021
## HANDWASHING PROCEDURE

Children and staff members shall wash their hands using the following method:

a) Check to be sure a clean, disposable paper (or single-use cloth) towel is available.

b) Turn on warm water, no less than 60 degrees F and no more than 120 degrees F, to a comfortable temperature.

c) Moisten hands with water and apply liquid soap to hands.

d) Rub hands together vigorously until a soapy lather appears, and continue for at least 10 seconds. Rub areas between fingers, around nailbeds, under fingernails, jewelry, and back of hands.

e) Rinse hands under running water, no less than 60 degrees F and no more than 120 degrees F, until they are free of soap and dirt. Leave the water running while drying hands.

f) Dry hands with the clean, disposable paper or single use cloth towel.

g) If taps do not shut off automatically, turn taps off with a disposable paper or single use cloth towel.

h) Throw the disposable paper towel into a lined trash container; or place single-use cloth towels in the laundry hamper; or hang individually labeled cloth towels to dry. Use hand lotion to prevent chapping of hands, if desired.

TYPE OF FACILITY: *Center; Large Family Child Care Home; Small Family Child Care Home*

## STANDARD 3.022
## ASSISTING CHILDREN WITH HANDWASHING

Caregivers shall provide assistance with handwashing at a sink for infants who can be safely cradled in one arm and for children who can stand but not wash their hands independently. A child who can stand shall either use a child-size sink or stand on a safety step at a height at which the child's hands can hang freely under the running water. After assisting the

Rationale, comments and references for each Standard are located in *Caring for Our Children, 2nd Edition* (http://nrc.uchsc.edu/CFOC/index.html)

child with handwashing, the staff member shall wash his or her own hands.
If a child is unable to stand and is too heavy to hold safely to wash the hands at the sink, caregivers shall use the following method:

- Wipe the child's hands with a damp paper towel moistened with a drop of liquid soap. Then discard the towel.
- Wipe the child's hands with a clean, wet, paper towel until the hands are free of soap. Then discard the towel.
- Dry the child's hands with a clean paper towel.

TYPE OF FACILITY: *Center; Large Family Child Care Home; Small Family Child Care Home*

## STANDARD 3.024
## PROCEDURE FOR NASAL SECRETIONS

Staff members and children shall blow or wipe their noses with disposable, one-use tissues and then discard them in a plastic-lined, covered, hands-free trash container. After blowing the nose, they shall wash their hands, as specified in STANDARD 3.021 and STANDARD 3.022.

TYPE OF FACILITY: *Center; Large Family Child Care Home; Small Family Child Care Home*

## STANDARD 3.026
## PREVENTION OF EXPOSURE TO BLOOD AND BODILY FLUIDS

Child care facilities shall adopt a modified version of Standard Precautions developed for use in hospitals by The Centers for Disease Control and Prevention as defined in this standard and as may be recommended by the Centers for Disease Control and Prevention for child care settings in the future. This modified version of Standard Precautions shall be used to handle potential exposure to blood, including the blood-containing body fluids and tissue discharges, and to handle other potentially infectious fluids.

In child care settings, exceptions to Standard Precautions as defined by the Centers for Disease Control and Prevention for hospital settings shall include:
a) Use of non-porous gloves is optional unless blood or blood containing body fluids may be involved. Gloves are not required for feeding human milk or cleaning up of spills of human milk.

b) Gowns and masks are not required.

c) Sufficient barriers include materials such as disposable diaper table paper that is moisture resistant, and non-porous gloves.

The staff shall be educated regarding routine precautions to prevent transmission of bloodborne pathogens before beginning to work in the facility and at least annually thereafter. The staff training shall comply with requirements of the Occupational Safety and Health Administration (OSHA), where applicable.

Procedures for Standard Precautions shall include:

a) Surfaces that may come in contact with potentially infectious body fluids must be disposable or of a material that can be sanitized. Use of materials that can be sterilized is not required.

b) The staff shall use barriers and techniques that:

1) Minimize potential contact of mucous membranes or openings in skin to blood or other potentially infectious body fluids and tissue discharges and

2) Reduce the spread of infectious material within the child care facility.

Such techniques include avoiding touching surfaces with potentially contaminated materials unless those surfaces are sanitized before further contact occurs with them by other objects or individuals.

c) When spills of body fluids, urine, feces, blood, saliva, nasal discharge, eye discharge, injury or tissue discharges, and human milk occur, these spills shall be cleaned up immediately, and further managed as follows:

1) For spills of vomit, urine, human milk, and feces, all floors, walls, bathrooms, tabletops, toys, kitchen counter tops, and diaper-changing tables in contact shall be cleaned and sanitized as for the procedure for diaper changing tables in STANDARD 3.014, Step 7.;

2) For spills of blood or other potentially infectious body fluids, including injury and tissue discharges, the area shall be cleaned and sanitized. Care shall be taken to avoid splashing any contaminated materials onto any mucus membrane (eyes, nose, mouth);

3) Blood-contaminated material and diapers shall be disposed of in a plastic bag with a secure tie.

4) Floors, rugs and carpeting that have been contaminated by body fluids shall be cleaned by blotting to remove the fluid as quickly as possible, then sanitized by spot-cleaning with a detergent-disinfectant, and shampooing, or steam-cleaning the contaminated surface.

TYPE OF FACILITY: *Center; Large Family Child Care Home; Small Family Child Care Home*

Rationale, comments and references for each Standard are located in *Caring for Our Children, 2nd Edition* (http://nrc.uchsc.edu/CFOC/index.html)

## STANDARD 3.027
# FEEDING OF HUMAN MILK TO ANOTHER MOTHER'S CHILD

If a child has been fed another child's bottle of expressed human milk, this shall be treated as an accidental exposure to a potential HIV-containing body fluid. Providers shall:

a) Inform the parents of the child who was given the wrong bottle that:
   1) Their child was given another child's bottle of expressed human milk;
   2) The risk of transmission of HIV is very small;
   3) They should notify the child's physician of the exposure;
   4) The child should have a baseline test for HIV and a follow-up test six months later.
   5) The mother of the child should have an HIV test immediately and a follow-up test six months later.

b) Inform the mother who expressed the human milk of the bottle switch and ask:
   1) If she has ever had an HIV test and, if so, if she would be willing to share the results with the parents of the exposed child;
   2) If she does not know if she has ever had an HIV test, if she would be willing to contact her obstetrician and find out, and if she has, share the results with the parents;
   3) If she has never had an HIV test, if she would be willing to have one immediately and a follow-up test six months later and share results with the parents;
   4) If the mother has had a previous test more than six months prior to the incident, if she would be willing to have a test immediately and a follow-up test six months later and share results with the parents;
   5) When the human milk was expressed and how it was handled before being brought to the facility.

TYPE OF FACILITY: *Center; Large Family Child Care Home; Small Family Child Care Home*

## STANDARD 3.028
# ROUTINE FREQUENCY OF CLEANING AND SANITATION

The routine frequency of cleaning and sanitation in the facility shall be as indicated in the table below. This frequency shall be increased from baseline routine frequencies whenever there are outbreaks of illness, there is known contamination, visible soil, or when recommended by the health department to control certain infectious diseases. All surfaces, furnishings, and equipment that are not in good repair or that have been contaminated by body fluids shall be taken out of service until they are repaired, cleaned, and, if contaminated, sanitized effectively.

TYPE OF FACILITY: *Center; Large Family Child Care Home; Small Family Child Care Home*

## STANDARD 3.029
## POTTY CHAIRS

Use of potty chairs shall be discouraged. If potty chairs are used, they shall be emptied into a toilet, cleaned in a utility sink, sanitized after each use, and stored in the bathroom. After the potty is sanitized, the utility sink shall also be sanitized.

TYPE OF FACILITY: *Center; Large Family Child Care Home; Small Family Child Care Home*

## STANDARD 3.031
## RAGS AND DISPOSABLE TOWELS USED FOR CLEANING

Disposable towels shall be preferred for cleaning. If clean reusable rags are used, they shall be laundered separately between uses for cleaning. Disposable towels shall be sealed in a plastic bag and removed to outside garbage. Cloth rags shall be placed in a closed, foot-operated receptacle until laundering.

TYPE OF FACILITY: *Center; Large Family Child Care Home; Small Family Child Care Home*

## STANDARD 3.036
## USE OF TOYS THAT CAN BE WASHED AND SANITIZED

Toys that cannot be washed and sanitized shall not be used. Toys that children have placed in their mouths or that are otherwise contaminated by body secretion or excretion shall be set aside where children cannot access them. They must be set aside until they are washed with water and detergent, rinsed, sanitized, and air-dried by hand or in a mechanical

Rationale, comments and references for each Standard are located in *Caring for Our Children, 2nd Edition* (http://nrc.uchsc.edu/CFOC/index.html)

dishwasher that meets the requirements of STANDARD 4.063 through STANDARD 4.065. Play with plastic or play foods shall be closely supervised to prevent shared mouthing of these toys.

Machine washable cloth toys shall be for use by one individual only until these toys are laundered.

Indoor toys shall not be shared between groups of infants or toddlers unless they are washed and sanitized before being moved from one group to the other.

TYPE OF FACILITY: *Center; Large Family Child Care Home; Small Family Child Care Home*

## STANDARD 3.037
## OBJECTS INTENDED FOR THE MOUTH

Thermometers, pacifiers, teething toys, and similar objects shall be cleaned and reusable parts shall be sanitized between uses. Pacifiers shall not be shared.

TYPE OF FACILITY: *Center; Large Family Child Care Home; Small Family Child Care Home*

## STANDARD 3.038
## ROUTINE CHECKS OF PLAY EQUIPMENT

A staff member shall be assigned to check all play equipment at least monthly to ensure that it is safe for children. In addition, the staff shall observe equipment while children are playing on it to ensure that it is safe for children.

TYPE OF FACILITY: *Center; Large Family Child Care Home; Small Family Child Care Home*

## STANDARD 3.041
## TOBACCO USE AND PROHIBITED SUBSTANCES

Tobacco use, alcohol, and illegal drugs shall be prohibited on the premises of the facility at all times.

TYPE OF FACILITY: *Center; Large Family Child Care Home; Small Family Child Care Home*

## STANDARD 3.045
## SUPERVISION NEAR BODIES OF WATER

Children shall not be permitted to play without constant supervision in areas where there is any body of water, including swimming pools, built-in wading pools, tubs, pails, sinks, or toilets, ponds and irrigation ditches.

Children who need assistance with toileting shall not be allowed in toilet or bathroom facilities without direct visual supervision. Children less than 5 years of age shall not be left unattended in a bathtub or shower.

TYPE OF FACILITY: *Center; Large Family Child Care Home; Small Family Child Care Home*

## STANDARD 3.048
## EMERGENCY PROCEDURES

When an immediate response is required, the following emergency procedures shall be utilized:
a)  First aid shall be employed, and the emergency medical response team shall be called, as indicated;
b)  The facility shall implement a plan for emergency transportation to a local hospital or health care facility;
c)  The parent or parent's emergency contact person shall be called as soon as practical;
d)  A staff member shall accompany the child to the hospital and will stay with the child until the parent or emergency contact person arrives.

TYPE OF FACILITY: *Center; Large Family Child Care Home; Small Family Child Care Home*

## STANDARD 3.049
## WRITTEN PLAN FOR MEDICAL EMERGENCY

Facilities shall have a written plan for immediate management and rapid access to medical care as appropriate to the situation. This plan shall:

Rationale, comments and references for each Standard are located in *Caring for Our Children, 2nd Edition* (http://nrc.uchsc.edu/CFOC/index.html)

a)  Describe for each child any special emergency procedures that will be used, if required, by the caregiver or by a physician or registered nurse available to the caregiver;

b)  Note any special medical procedures, if required by the child's condition, that will be used or might be required for the child while he/she is in the facility's care, including the possibility of a need for cardiac resuscitation;

c)  Include in a separate format, any information to be given to an emergency responder in the event that one must be called to the facility for the child. This information shall include:

    1)  Any special information needed by the emergency responder to respond appropriately to the child's condition;

    2)  A listing of the child's health care providers in the event of an emergency.

TYPE OF FACILITY: *Center; Large Family Child Care Home; Small Family Child Care Home*

## STANDARD 3.053
## REPORTING SUSPECTED CHILD ABUSE, NEGLECT, EXPLOITATION

The facility shall report to the department of social services, child protective services, or police as required by state and local laws, in any instance where there is reasonable cause to believe that child abuse, neglect, or exploitation may have occurred.

TYPE OF FACILITY: *Center; Large Family Child Care Home; Small Family Child Care Home*

## STANDARD 3.055
## IMMUNITY OF REPORTERS OF CHILD ABUSE FROM SANCTION

Caregivers who report abuse in the settings where they work shall be immune from discharge, retaliation, or other disciplinary action for that reason alone, unless it is proven that the report was malicious.

TYPE OF FACILITY: *Center*

## STANDARD 3.059
## FACILITY LAYOUT TO REDUCE RISK OF ABUSE

The physical layout of facilities shall be arranged so that all areas can be viewed by at least one other adult in addition to the caregiver at all times when children are in care. Such a layout reduces the risk of abuse and likelihood of extended periods of time in isolation for individual caregivers with children, especially in areas where children may be partially undressed or in the nude.

Video surveillance equipment, parabolic mirrors, or other devices designed to improve visual access shall be installed to enhance safety for the children.

*Editor's Note: This standard applies to outdoor areas as well.*

TYPE OF FACILITY: *Center*

## STANDARD 3.060
## SEIZURE CARE PLAN

The child care facility shall have a seizure care plan and ensure that all caregivers receive training to successfully implement the plan. If a child in care has epilepsy or a history of febrile seizures that are not considered a form of epilepsy, the child's seizure care plan shall include the following:
a)   Types of seizures the child has (such as partial, generalized, or unclassified), as well as a description of the manifestation of these types of seizures in this child;
b)   The current treatment regimen for this child, including medications, doses, schedule of administration, guidelines, route of administration, and potential side effects for routine and as-needed medications;
c)   Restrictions from activities that:
   1)   Could be dangerous if the child were to have a seizure during the activity;
   2)   Could precipitate a seizure (examples include swimming and falling from a height);
d)   Recognizing and providing first aid for a seizure;
e)   Guidelines on when emergency medical help should be sought for the child who has epilepsy, such as:
   1)   A major convulsive seizure lasting more than 5 minutes;
   2)   One seizure after another without waking up between seizures;
   3)   The child is completely unresponsive for 20 minutes after the seizure;
f)   Documentation in the child's health report that indicates:

Rationale, comments and references for each Standard are located in *Caring for Our Children, 2nd Edition* (http://nrc.uchsc.edu/CFOC/index.html)

    1) Whether the child has had a history of any type of *seizures*;
    2) Whether the child is currently taking medication to control the
       seizures;
    3) What observations caregivers should make to help the child's
       clinician adjust the medication;
    4) The type and frequency of reported seizures as well as seizures
       observed in the facility;
g) Plans for support of the child with epilepsy and the child's family.

TYPE OF FACILITY: *Center; Large Family Child Care Home; Small Family Child Care Home*

## STANDARD 3.061
## TRAINING FOR STAFF TO HANDLE SEIZURES

Staff members shall be trained in, and shall be prepared to follow, the prescribed procedure when a child has a seizure. These procedures include proper positioning, keeping the airway open, and knowing when and whom to call for medical assistance. All staff members shall be instructed about the relevant side effects of any anti-convulsant medications that children in the facility take and how to observe and report them.

Telephone numbers for emergency care shall be posted, as specified in Posting Documents, STANDARD 8.077.

TYPE OF FACILITY: *Center; Large Family Child Care Home; Small Family Child Care Home*

## STANDARD 3.062
## MANAGEMENT OF CHILDREN WITH ASTHMA

When a child who has had a diagnosis of asthma by a health professional attends the child care facility, the following actions shall occur:
a) Each child with asthma shall have a special care plan prepared for the facility by the child's source of health care, to include:
    1) Written instructions regarding how to avoid the conditions that
       are known to trigger asthma symptoms for the child;
    2) Indications for treatment of the child's asthma in the child care
       facility;
    3) Names, doses, and method of administration of any medications,
       e.g., inhalers, the child should receive for an acute episode and
       for ongoing prevention;

4) When the next update of the special care plan is due;

b) Based on the child's special care plan, the child's caregivers shall receive training, demonstrate competence in, and implement measures for:

1) Preventing exposure of the asthmatic child to conditions likely to trigger the child's asthma;
2) Recognizing the symptoms of asthma;
3) Treating acute episodes;

c) Parents and staff shall arrange for the facility to have necessary medications and equipment to manage the child's asthma while the child is at the child care facility;

d) Properly trained caregivers shall promptly and properly administer prescribed medications according to the training provided and in accordance with the special care plan;

e) The facility shall notify parents of any change in asthma symptoms when that change occurs. See the *Special Care Plan for a Child with Asthma*, Appendix M;

f) The facility shall try to reduce these common asthma triggers by:

1) Encouraging the use of allergen impermeable nap mats or crib/mattress covers;
2) Prohibiting pets (particularly furred or feathered pets);
3) Prohibiting smoking inside the facility or on the playground;
4) Discouraging the use of perfumes, scented cleaning products, and other fumes;
5) Quickly fixing leaky plumbing or other sources of excess water;
6) Ensuring frequent vacuuming of carpet and upholstered furniture at times when the children are not present;
7) Storing all food in airtight containers, cleaning up all food crumbs or spilled liquids, and properly disposing of garbage and trash;
8) Using integrated pest management techniques to get rid of pests (using the least hazardous treatments first and progressing to more toxic treatments only as necessary);
9) Keeping children indoors when local weather forecasts predict unhealthy ozone levels or high pollen counts.

TYPE OF FACILITY: *Center; Large Family Child Care Home; Small Family Child Care Home*

# STANDARD 3.063
# CARING FOR CHILDREN WHO REQUIRE MEDICAL PROCEDURES

A facility that enrolls children who require tube feedings, endotrachial suctioning, oxygen, postural drainage, or catheterization daily (unless the child requiring catheterization can perform this function on his/her own)

Rationale, comments and references for each Standard are located in *Caring for Our Children, 2nd Edition* (http://nrc.uchsc.edu/CFOC/index.html)

or any other special medical procedures performed routinely, or who might require special procedures on an urgent basis, shall receive a written report from the health care provider who prescribed the special treatment (such as a urologist for catheterization). A facility shall receive a written report from the child's clinician about any special preparation to perform urgent procedures other than those that might be required for a typical child, such as cardiac resuscitation. This report shall include instructions for performing the procedure, how to receive training in performing the procedure, and what to do and who to notify if complications occur. Training for the child care staff shall be provided by a qualified health care professional in accordance with state practice acts.

TYPE OF FACILITY: *Center; Large Family Child Care; Small Family Child Care Home*

# STANDARD 3.065
# INCLUSION/EXCLUSION/DISMISSAL OF CHILDREN

The parent, legal guardian, or other person the parent authorizes shall be notified immediately when a child has any sign or symptom that requires exclusion from the facility. The facility shall ask the parents to consult with the child's health care provider. The child care provider shall ask the parents to inform them of the advice received from the health care provider. The advice of the child's health care provider shall be followed by the child care facility.

With the exception of head lice for which exclusion at the end of the day is appropriate, a facility shall temporarily exclude a child or send the child home as soon as possible if one or more of the following conditions exists:

a) The illness prevents the child from participating comfortably in activities as determined by the child care provider;

b) The illness results in a greater need for care than the child care staff can provide without compromising the health and safety of the other children as determined by the child care provider;

c) The child has any of the following conditions:

1) Fever, accompanied by behavior changes or other signs or symptoms of illness until medical professional evaluation finds the child able to be included at the facility;

2) Symptoms and signs of possible severe illness until medical professional evaluation finds the child able to included at the facility. Symptoms and signs of possible severe illness shall include
 • lethargy that is more than expected tiredness,
 • uncontrolled coughing,

- inexplicable irritability or persistent crying,
- difficult breathing,
- wheezing, or
- other unusual signs for the child;

3) Diarrhea, defined by more watery stools, decreased form of stool that is not associated with changes of diet, and increased frequency of passing stool, that is not contained by the child's ability to use the toilet. Children with diarrheal illness of infectious origin generally may be allowed to return to child care once the diarrhea resolves, except for children with diarrhea caused by *Salmonella typhi*, *Shigella* or *E. coli 0157:H7*. For *Salmonella typhi*, 3 negative stool cultures are required. For *Shigella* or *E. coli 0157:H7*, two negative stool cultures are required. Children whose stools remain loose but who, otherwise, seem well and whose stool cultures are negative, need not be excluded. See also Child-Specific Procedures for Enteric (Diarrheal) and Hepatitis A Virus (HAV) Infections, STANDARD 6.023, for additional separation and exclusion information for children with diarrhea; STANDARD 3.066, on separate care for these children; and STANDARD 3.084 and STANDARD 3.087, on notifying parents;

4) Blood in stools not explainable by dietary change, medication, or hard stools;

5) Vomiting illness (two or more episodes of vomiting in the previous 24 hours) until vomiting resolves or until a health care provider determines that the cause of the vomiting is not contagious and the child is not in danger of dehydration. See also STANDARD 3.066, on separate care for these children;

6) Persistent abdominal pain (continues more than 2 hours) or intermittent pain associated with fever or other signs or symptoms;

7) Mouth sores with drooling, unless a health care provider or health department official determines that the child is noninfectious;

8) Rash with fever or behavior change, until a physician determines that these symptoms do not indicate a communicable disease;

9) Purulent conjunctivitis (defined as pink or red conjunctiva with white or yellow eye discharge), until after treatment has been initiated. In epidemics of nonpurulent pink eye, exclusion shall be required only if the health authority recommends it;

10) Pediculosis (head lice), from the end of the day until after the first treatment. See STANDARD 6.038;

11) Scabies, until after treatment has been completed. See STANDARD 6.037;

12) Tuberculosis, until a health care provider or health official states that the child is on appropriate therapy and can attend child care. See STANDARD 6.014 and STANDARD 6.015;

Rationale, comments and references for each Standard are located in *Caring for Our Children, 2nd Edition* (http://nrc.uchsc.edu/CFOC/index.html)

13) Impetigo, until 24 hours after treatment has been initiated;

14) Strep throat or other streptococcal infection, until 24 hours after initial antibiotic treatment and cessation of fever. See also Group A Streptococcal (GAS) Infection, STANDARD 6.012 and STANDARD 6.013;

15) Varicella-Zoster (Chickenpox), until all sores have dried and crusted (usually 6 days). See also STANDARD 6.019 and STANDARD 6.020;

16) Pertussis, until 5 days of appropriate antibiotic treatment (currently, erythromycin, which is given for 14 consecutive days) has been completed. See STANDARD 6.009 and STANDARD 6.010;

17) Mumps, until 9 days after onset of parotid gland swelling;

18) Hepatitis A virus, until 1 week after onset of illness, jaundice, or as directed by the health department when passive immunoprophylaxis (currently, immune serum globulin) has been administered to appropriate children and staff members. See STANDARD 6.023 through STANDARD 6.026;

19) Measles, until 4 days after onset of rash;

20) Rubella, until 6 days after onset of rash;

21) Unspecified respiratory tract illness, see STANDARD 6.017;

22) Shingles (herpes zoster). See STANDARD 6.020;

23) Herpes simplex, see STANDARD 6.018.

Some states have regulations governing isolation of persons with communicable diseases including some of those listed here. Providers shall contact their health consultant or health department for information regarding isolation of children with diseases such as chickenpox, pertussis, mumps, hepatitis A, measles, rubella, and tuberculosis. If different health care professionals give conflicting opinions about the need to exclude an ill child on the basis of the risk of transmission of infection to other children, the health department shall make the determination.

The child care provider shall make the decision about whether a child meets or does not meet the exclusion criteria for participation and the child's need for care relative to the staff's ability to provide care. If parents and the child care staff disagree, and the reason for exclusion relates to the child's ability to participate or the caregiver's ability to provide care for the other children, the child care provider shall not be required by a parent to accept responsibility for the care of the child during the period in which the child meets the providers's criteria for exclusion.

TYPE OF FACILITY: *Center; Large Family Child Care Home; Small Family Child Care Home*

# STANDARD 3.067
## OUTBREAK CONTROL

During the course of an identified outbreak of any communicable illness at the facility, a child shall be excluded if the health department official or health care provider suspects that the child is contributing to transmission of the illness at the facility. The child shall be readmitted when the health department official or health care provider who made the initial determination decides that the risk of transmission is no longer present.

TYPE OF FACILITY: *Center; Large Family Child Care Home; Small Family Child Care Home*

# STANDARD 3.069
## STAFF EXCLUSION FOR ILLNESS

Please note that if a staff member has no contact with the children, or with anything with which the children come into contact, this standard does not apply to that staff member.

A facility shall not deny admission to or send home a staff member or substitute with illness unless one or more of the following conditions exists. The staff member shall be excluded as follows:
a) Chickenpox, until all lesions have dried and crusted, which usually occurs by 6 days;
b) Shingles, only if the lesions cannot be covered by clothing or a dressing until the lesions have crusted;
c) Rash with fever or joint pain, until diagnosed not to be measles or rubella;
d) Measles, until 4 days after onset of the rash (if the staff member or substitute is immunocompetent);
e) Rubella, until 6 days after onset of rash;
f) Diarrheal illness, three or more episodes of diarrhea during the previous 24 hours or blood in stools, until diarrhea resolves; if *E.coli 0157:H7* or *Shigella* is isolated, until diarrhea resolves and two stool cultures are negative;
g) Vomiting illness, two or more episodes of vomiting during the previous 24 hours, until vomiting resolves or is determined to result from noncommunicable conditions such as pregnancy or a digestive disorder;
h) Hepatitis A virus, until 1 week after onset or as directed by the health department when immunoglobulin has been given to appropriate children and staff in the facility;
i) Pertussis, until after 5 days of appropriate antibiotic therapy (which is to be given for a total of 14 days) and until disease preventive

Rationale, comments and references for each Standard are located in *Caring for Our Children, 2nd Edition* (http://nrc.uchsc.edu/CFOC/index.html)

measures, including preventive antibiotics and vaccines for children and staff who have been in contact with children infected with pertussis, have been implemented;

j)  Skin infection (such as impetigo), until 24 hours after treatment has been initiated;

k)  Tuberculosis, until noninfectious and cleared by a health department official;

l)  Strep throat or other streptococcal infection, until 24 hours after initial antibiotic treatment and end of fever;

m) Head lice, from the end of the day of discovery until after the first treatment;

n)  Scabies, until after treatment has been completed;

o)  Purulent conjunctivitis, defined as pink or red conjunctiva with white or yellow eye discharge, often with matted eyelids after sleep, and including eye pain or redness of the eyelids or skin surrounding the eye, until 24 hours after treatment has been initiated;

p)  *Haemophilus influenzae* type b (Hib), prophylaxis, until antibiotic treatment has been initiated;

q)  Meningococcal infection, until all staff members, for whom antibiotic prophylaxis has been recommended, have been treated. See STANDARD 6.006 through STANDARD 6.008;

r)  Respiratory illness, if the illness limits the staff member's ability to provide an acceptable level of child care and compromises the health and safety of the children.

Child care providers who have herpes cold sores shall not be excluded from the child care facility, but shall:

1)  Cover and not touch their lesions;

2)  Carefully observe handwashing policies;

3)  Refrain from kissing or nuzzling infants or children, especially children with dermatitis.

TYPE OF FACILITY: *Center; Large Family Child Care Home; Small Family Child Care Home*

## STANDARD 3.070
## SPACE REQUIREMENTS FOR CARE OF ILL CHILDREN

Environmental space utilized for the care of children who are ill with infectious diseases and cannot receive care in their usual child care group shall meet all requirements for well children and include the following additional requirements:

a)  If the program for ill children is in the same facility as the well-child program, well children shall not use or share furniture, fixtures, equipment, or supplies designated for use with ill children unless it has been cleaned and sanitized before use by well children;

b) Indoor space that the facility uses for ill children, including hallways, bathrooms, and kitchens, shall be separate from indoor space used with well children; this reduces the likelihood of mixing supplies, toys, and equipment. The facility may use a single kitchen for ill and well children if the kitchen is staffed by a cook who has no child care responsibilities other than food preparation and who does not handle soiled dishes and utensils until after food preparation and food service are completed for any meal;

c) Children whose symptoms indicate infections of the gastrointestinal tract (often with diarrhea) or liver, who receive care in special facilities for ill children shall receive this care in a space separate from other children with other illnesses to reduce the likelihood of disease being transmitted between children by limiting child-to-child interaction, separating staff responsibilities, and not mixing supplies, toys, and equipment;

d) If the facility cares for children with chickenpox, these children shall receive care in a separate room that is ventilated externally.

e) Each child care room shall have a handwashing sink that can provide a steady stream of water, no less than 60 degrees F and no more than 120 degrees F, at least for 10 seconds. Soap and disposable paper towels shall be available at the handwashing sink at all times.

f) Each room where children who wear diapers receive care shall have its own diaper changing area adjacent to a handwashing sink.

TYPE OF FACILITY: *Center; Large Family Child Care Home; Small Family Child Care Home*

## STANDARD 3.078
## INCLUSION AND EXCLUSION OF CHILDREN FROM FACILITIES THAT SERVE ILL CHILDREN

Facilities that care for ill children who have conditions that require additional attention from the caregiver shall arrange for or ask the health consultant to arrange for a clinical health evaluation, by a licensed health care professional, for each child who is admitted to the facility. These facilities shall include children with conditions listed in STANDARD 3.065 if their policies and plans address the management of these conditions, except for the following conditions which require exclusion from all types of child care facilities that are not medical care institutions (such as hospitals or skilled nursing facilities):

a) Fever and a stiff neck, lethargy, irritability, or persistent crying;

b) Diarrhea (three or more loose stools in an 8-hour period or more stools compared to the child's normal pattern, with more stool water or less form) and one or more of the following:
   1) Signs of dehydration;

2) Blood or mucus in the stool, unless at least one stool culture demonstrates absence of *Shigella, Salmonella, Campylobacter,* and *E. coli 0157:H7*. See STANDARD 3.065 and STANDARD 6.023;

3) Diarrhea attributable to *Salmonella, Campylobacter, or Giardia* except that a child with diarrhea attributable to *Campylobacter or Giardia* may be readmitted 24 hours after treatment has been initiated if cleared by the child's physician;

c) Diarrhea attributable to *Shigella* and *E. coli 0157:H7*, until diarrhea resolves and two stool cultures taken 48 hours apart are negative;

d) Vomiting three or more times, or signs of dehydration;

e) Contagious stages of pertusis, measles, mumps, chickenpox, rubella, or diphtheria, unless the child is appropriately isolated from children with other illnesses and cared for only with children having the same illness;

f) Untreated infestation of scabies or head lice;

g) Untreated tuberculosis;

h) Undiagnosed rash;

i) Abdominal pain that is intermittent or persistent;

j) Difficulty in breathing;

k) Lethargy such that the child does not play;

l) Undiagnosed jaundice (yellow skin and whites of eyes);

m) Other conditions as may be determined by the director or health consultant.

TYPE OF FACILITY: *Center; Large Family Child Care Home; Small Family Child Care Home*

## STANDARD 3.081
## PERMISSIBLE ADMINISTRATION OF MEDICATION

The administration of medicines at the facility shall be limited to:

a) Prescribed medications ordered by a health care provider for a specific child, with written permission of the parent or legal guardian;

b) Nonprescription (over-the-counter) medications recommended by a health care provider for a specific child or for a specific circumstance for any child in the facility, with written permission of the parent or legal guardian.

TYPE OF FACILITY: *Center; Large Family Child Care Home; Small Family Child Care Home*

## STANDARD 3.082
## LABELING AND STORAGE OF MEDICATIONS

Any prescribed medication brought into the facility by the parent, legal guardian, or responsible relative of a child shall be dated, and shall be kept in the original container. The container shall be labeled by a pharmacist with:
a)   The child's first and last names;
b)   The date the prescription was filled;
c)   The name of the health care provider who wrote the prescription, the medication's expiration date;
d)   The manufacturer's instructions or prescription label with specific, legible instructions for administration, storage, and disposal;
e)   The name and strength of the medication.
Over-the-counter medications shall be kept in the original container as sold by the manufacturer, labeled by the parent, with the child's name and specific instructions given by the child's health professional for administration.

All medications, refrigerated or unrefrigerated, shall have child-resistant caps, shall be kept in an organized fashion, shall be stored away from food at the proper temperature, and shall be inaccessible to children. Medication shall not be used beyond the date of expiration.

TYPE OF FACILITY: *Center; Large Family Child Care Home; Small Family Child Care Home*

## STANDARD 3.083
## TRAINING OF CAREGIVERS TO ADMINISTER MEDICATION

Any caregiver who administers medication shall be trained to:
a)   Check that the name of the child on the medication and the child receiving the medication are the same;
b)   Read and understand the label/prescription directions in relation to the measured dose, frequency, and other circumstances relative to administration (such as in relation to meals);
c)   Administer the medication according to the prescribed methods and the prescribed dose;
d)   Observe and report any side effects from medications;
e)   Document the administration of each dose by the time and the amount given.

TYPE OF FACILITY: *Center; Large Family Child Care Home; Small Family Child Care Home*

## STANDARD 3.086
## NOTIFICATION OF THE FACILITY ABOUT COMMUNICABLE DISEASE OR OTHER PROBLEMS BY PARENTS

Upon registration of each child, the facility shall inform parents that parents must notify the facility within 24 hours after their child or any member of the immediate household has developed a known or suspected communicable disease as required by the health department. When the child has a disease requiring exclusion or dismissal, the parents shall inform the facility of the diagnosis.
The facility shall encourage parents to inform the caregivers of any other problems which may affect the child's behavior.

TYPE OF FACILITY: *Center; Large Family Child Care Home; Small Family Child Care Home*

## STANDARD 3.088
## WRITTEN POLICY FOR REPORTING ILLNESS TO THE HEALTH DEPARTMENT

The facility shall have a written policy that complies with the state's reporting requirements for ill children. All communicable diseases shall be reported to the health department. The facility shall have the telephone number of the responsible health authority to whom confirmed or suspected cases of these diseases, or outbreaks of other communicable diseases, shall be reported, and shall designate a staff member as responsible for reporting the disease.

TYPE OF FACILITY: *Center; Large Family Child Care Home; Small Family Child Care Home*

## STANDARD 3.089
## DEATH (SIDS AND OTHER)

If a facility experiences the death of a child, the following shall be done:
a)   If the child dies while at the facility:
   1)   Immediately notify emergency medical personnel;
   2)   Immediately notify the child's parents;
   3)   Notify the Licensing agency;
   4)   Provide age appropriate information for children and parents;
b)   For a suspected Sudden Infant Death Syndrome (SIDS) death or other unexplained deaths:

1) Seek support and information from local, state, or national SIDS resources;
2) Provide SIDS information to the parents of the other children in the facility;
3) Provide age-appropriate information to the other children in the facility;

c) If the child dies while not at the facility:
1) Provide age-appropriate information for children and parents;
2) Make resources for support available to parents and children.

d) Release specific information about the circumstances of the child's death that the child's family agrees the facility may share.

TYPE OF FACILITY: *Center; Large Family Child Care Home; Small Family Child Care Home*

# CHAPTER 4 - NUTRITION AND FOOD SERVICE

## STANDARD 4.006
## AVAILABILITY OF DRINKING WATER

Clean, sanitary drinking water shall be readily available throughout the day.

TYPE OF FACILITY: *Center; Large Family Child Care Home; Small Family Child Care Home*

## STANDARD 4.008
## WRITTEN MENUS, INTRODUCTION OF NEW FOODS

Facilities shall develop, at least one month in advance, written menus showing all foods to be served during that month and shall make them available to parents. The facility shall date and retain these menus; amended to reflect any changes in the food actually served. Any substitutions shall be of equal nutrient value.

To avoid problems of food sensitivity in very young children, child care providers shall obtain from the child's parents, a list of foods that have already been introduced (without any reaction), and then serve some of these foods to the child. As new foods are introduced, child care providers shall share and discuss these foods with the parents prior to their introduction.

TYPE OF FACILITY: *Center; Large Family Child Care Home; Small Family Child Care Home*

## STANDARD 4.009
## FEEDING PLANS

Before any child enters a child care facility, the facility shall obtain a written history of any special nutrition or feeding needs the child has. The staff shall review this history with the child's parents. If further information is required, along with the parents' written consent, the program may consult with the child's primary health care provider.

The written history of special nutrition or feeding needs shall be used to develop individual feeding plans and, collectively, to develop facility menus. Disciplines related to special nutrition needs, including nursing, speech, and occupational and physical therapy, shall participate when needed and/or when they are available to the facility. With the exception of children on special diets, the general nutrition guidelines for facilities in General Requirements, STANDARD 4.001 through STANDARD 4.010; Nutrition for Infants, STANDARD 4.011 through STANDARD 4.021; Nutrition for Toddlers and Preschoolers, STANDARD 4.022 through STANDARD 4.024; and Nutrition for School-age Children, STANDARD 4.025, shall be applied.

The feeding plan shall include steps to take when a situation arises that requires rapid response by the staff (such as a child's choking during mealtime or a child with a known history of food allergies demonstrating signs and symptoms of anaphylaxis). The completed plan shall be on file and accessible to the staff.

TYPE OF FACILITY: *Center; Large Family Child Care Home; Small Family Child Care Home*

## STANDARD 4.010
## CARE FOR CHILDREN WITH FOOD ALLERGIES

When children with food allergies attend the child care facility, the following shall occur:
a)  Each child with a food allergy shall have a special care plan prepared for the facility by the child's source of health care, to include:

1) Written instructions regarding the food(s) to which the child is allergic and steps that need to be taken to avoid that food;
2) A detailed treatment plan to be implemented in the event of an allergic reaction, including the names, doses, and methods of administration of any medications that the child should receive in the event of a reaction. The plan shall include specific symptoms that would indicate the need to administer one or more medications;

b) Based on the child's special care plan, the child's caregivers shall receive training, demonstrate competence in, and implement measures for:
   1) Preventing exposure to the specific food(s) to which the child is allergic;
   2) Recognizing the symptoms of an allergic reaction;
   3) Treating allergic reactions;

c) Parents and staff shall arrange for the facility to have necessary medications, proper storage of such medications, and the equipment and training to manage the child's food allergy while the child is at the child care facility;

d) Caregivers shall promptly and properly administer prescribed medications in the event of an allergic reaction according to the instructions in the special care plan;

e) The facility shall notify the parents of any suspected allergic reactions, the ingestion of the problem food, or contact with the problem food, even if a reaction did not occur;

f) The facility shall notify the child's physician if the child has required treatment by the facility for a food allergic reaction;

g) The facility shall contact the emergency medical services system immediately whenever epinephrine has been administered;

h) Parents of all children in the child's class shall be advised to avoid any known allergies in class treats or special foods brought into the child care setting.

i) Individual child's food allergies shall be posted prominently in the classroom and/or wherever food is served.

j) On field trips or transport out of the child care setting, the written child care plan for the child with allergies shall be routinely carried.

TYPE OF FACILITY: *Center; Large Family Child Care Home; Small Family Child Care Home*

# STANDARD 4.014
## TECHNIQUES FOR BOTTLE FEEDING

When bottle feeding, caregivers shall either hold infants or feed them sitting up. Infants who are unable to sit shall always be held for bottle

Rationale, comments and references for each Standard are located in *Caring for Our Children, 2nd Edition* (http://nrc.uchsc.edu/CFOC/index.html)

feeding. The facility shall not permit infants to have bottles in the crib or to carry bottles with them either during the day or at night.

A caregiver shall not bottle feed more than one infant at a time.

TYPE OF FACILITY: *Center; Large Family Child Care Home; Small Family Child Care Home*

## STANDARD 4.015
## FEEDING HUMAN MILK

Expressed human milk shall be placed in a clean and sanitary bottle and nipple that fits tightly to prevent spilling during transport to home or facility. The bottle shall be properly labeled with the infant's name. The bottle shall immediately be stored in the refrigerator on arrival. Expressed human milk shall be discarded if it presents a threat to a baby such as:
- Human milk is in an unsanitary bottle;
- Human milk that has been unrefrigerated for an hour or more;
- A bottle of human milk that has been fed over a period that exceeds an hour from the beginning of the feeding.

TYPE OF FACILITY: *Center; Large Family Child Care Home; Small Family Child Care Home*

## STANDARD 4.017
## PREPARATION AND HANDLING OF BOTTLE FEEDING

Only cleaned and sanitized bottles, or their equivalent, and nipples shall be used. All filled containers of human milk shall be of the ready-to-feed type, identified with a label which won't come off in water or handling, bearing the date of collection and child's full name. The filled, labeled containers of human milk shall be kept frozen or refrigerated, and iron-fortified formula shall be refrigerated until immediately before feeding. Any contents remaining after a feeding shall be discarded. Prepared bottles of formula from powder or concentrate or ready-to-feed formula shall be labeled with the child's name and date of preparation, kept refrigerated, and shall be discarded after 48 hours if not used. An open container of ready-to-feed or concentrated formula shall be covered, refrigerated, and discarded after 48 hours if not used.

Unused expressed human milk shall be discarded after 48 hours if refrigerated, or by three months if frozen, and stored in a deep freezer at

0 degrees F. Unused frozen human milk which has been thawed in the refrigerator shall be used within 24 hours. Frozen human milk shall be thawed under running cold water or in the refrigerator.
Human milk from a mother shall be used only with that mother's own child.

A bottle that has been fed over a period that exceeds an hour from the beginning of the feeding or has been unrefrigerated an hour or more shall not be served to an infant.

TYPE OF FACILITY: Center; Large Family Child Care Home; Small Family Child Care Home

## STANDARD 4.018
## WARMING BOTTLES AND INFANT FOODS

Bottles and infant foods shall be warmed under running warm tap water or by placing them in a container of water that is no warmer than 120 degrees F. Bottles shall not be left in a pot of water to warm for more than 5 minutes. Bottles and infant foods shall not be warmed in a microwave oven. After warming, bottles shall be mixed gently and the temperature of the milk tested before feeding. Infant foods shall be stirred carefully to distribute the heat evenly. A caregiver shall not hold an infant while removing a bottle or infant food from the container of warm water or while preparing a bottle or stirring infant food that has been warmed in some other way.

If a slow-cooking device, such as a crock pot, is used for warming infant formula, human milk, or infant food, this slow-cooking device shall be out of children's reach, shall contain water at a temperature that does not exceed 120 degrees F. and shall be emptied, sanitized, and refilled with fresh water daily.

## STANDARD 4.034
## HOT LIQUIDS AND FOODS

Adults shall not consume hot liquids in child care areas. They shall keep hot liquids and hot foods out of the reach of infants, toddlers, and pre-schoolers. Adults shall not place hot liquids and foods at the edge of a counter or table, or on a tablecloth that could be yanked down, while the adult is holding or working with a child. Electrical cords from coffee pots shall not be allowed to hang within the reach of children. Food pre-parers shall position pot handles toward the back of the stove.

TYPE OF FACILITY: *Center; Large Family Child Care Home; Small Family Child Care Home*

## STANDARD 4.036
## LOCATION OF THE ADULT SUPERVISING CHILDREN FEEDING THEMSELVES

Children in mid-infancy who are learning to feed themselves shall be supervised by an adult seated within arm's reach of them at all times while being fed. Children over 12 months of age who can feed themselves shall be supervised by an adult who is seated at the same table or within arm's reach of the child's highchair or feeding table.

TYPE OF FACILITY: *Center; Large Family Child Care Home; Small Family Child Care Home*

## STANDARD 4.037
## FOOD THAT ARE CHOKING HAZARDS

Caregivers shall not offer to children under 4 years of age foods that are implicated in choking incidents (round, hard, small, thick and sticky, smooth, or slippery). Examples of these foods are hot dogs (whole or sliced into rounds), raw carrot rounds, whole grapes, hard candy, nuts, seeds, raw peas, hard pretzels, chips, peanuts, popcorn, marshmallows, spoonfuls of peanut butter, and chunks of meat larger than can be swallowed whole.

TYPE OF FACILITY: *Center; Large Family Child Care Home; Small Family Child Care Home*

## STANDARD 4.038
## PROGRESSION OF EXPERIENCES WITH FOOD TEXTURES

For infants, foods shall be fed which are age and developmentally appropriate. Foods shall progress from pureed to ground to finely mashed to finely chopped as an infant develops. When children are ready for chopped foods, these foods shall be cut into small pieces no larger than 1/4-inch cubes or thin slices. For toddlers, foods shall be cut up in small pieces no larger than 1/2-inch cubes.

TYPE OF FACILITY: *Center; Large Family Child Care Home; Small Family Child Care Home*

## STANDARD 4.039
## PROHIBITED USES OF FOOD

Caregivers shall encourage, but not force, children to eat. Caregivers shall not use food as a reward or punishment.

TYPE OF FACILITY: *Center; Large Family Child Care Home; Small Family Child Care Home*

## STANDARD 4.042
## FOOD PREPARATION AREA

The food preparation area of the kitchen shall be separate from eating, play, laundry, toilet, and bathroom areas and from areas where animals are permitted, and shall not be used as a passageway while food is being prepared. Food preparation areas shall be separated by a door, gate, counter, or room divider from areas the children use for activities unrelated to food, except in small family child care homes when separation may limit supervision of children.

Infants and toddlers shall not have access to the kitchen in child care centers. Access by older children to the kitchen of centers shall be permitted only when supervised by staff members who have been certified by the Child Care Nutrition Specialist (see Appendix C) or the center director as qualified to follow the facility's sanitation and safety procedures.

In all types of child care facilities, children shall never be in the kitchen unless they are directly supervised by a caregiver. Children of preschool-age and older shall be restricted from access to areas while hot food is being prepared. School-age children may engage in food preparation activities. Parents and other adults shall be permitted to use the kitchen only if they know and follow the food safety rules of the facility. The facility shall check with local health authorities about any additional regulations that apply.

TYPE OF FACILITY: *Center; Large Family Child Care Home; Small Family Child Care Home*

Rationale, comments and references for each Standard are located in *Caring for Our Children, 2nd Edition* (http://nrc.uchsc.edu/CFOC/index.html)

## STANDARD 4.044
# MAINTENANCE OF FOOD SERVICE SURFACES AND EQUIPMENT

All surfaces that come into contact with food, including tables and countertops, as well as floors and shelving in the food preparation area shall be in good repair, free of cracks or crevices, and shall be made of smooth, nonporous material that is kept clean and sanitized. All kitchen equipment shall be clean and shall be maintained in operable condition according to the manufacturer's guidelines for maintenance and operation. The facility shall maintain an inventory of food service equipment that includes the date of purchase, the warranty date, and a history of repairs.

TYPE OF FACILITY: *Center; Large Family Child Care Home; Small Family Child Care Home*

## STANDARD 4.051
# STAFF RESTRICTED FROM FOOD HANDLING

No one who has signs or symptoms of illness, including vomiting, diarrhea, and infectious skin sores that cannot be covered, or who potentially or actually is infected with bacteria, viruses or parasites that can be carried in food, shall be responsible for food handling. Plastic gloves, which shall be kept clean and replaced when soiled, shall be used when food is served by hand. No one with open or infected injuries shall work in the food preparation area unless the injuries are covered with nonporous (such as latex or vinyl) gloves.

In centers and large family child care homes, staff members who are involved in the process of preparing or handling food shall not change diapers. Staff members who work with diapered children shall not prepare or serve food for older groups of children. When staff members who are caring for infants and toddlers are responsible for changing diapers, they shall handle food only for the infants and toddlers in their groups and only after thoroughly washing their hands. Caregivers who prepare food shall wash their hands carefully before handling food, regardless of whether they change diapers. Plastic gloves shall be used in addition to handwashing. When caregivers must handle food, staffing assignments shall be made to foster completion of the food handling activities by caregivers of older children, or by caregivers of infants and toddlers before the caregiver assumes other caregiving duties for that day.

TYPE OF FACILITY: *Center; Large Family Child Care Home; Small Family Child Care Home*

# STANDARD 4.052
# PRECAUTIONS FOR A SAFE FOOD SUPPLY

All foods stored, prepared, or served shall be safe for human consumption by observation and smell. The following precautions shall be observed for a safe food supply:

a) Home-canned food, food from dented, rusted, bulging, or leaking cans, and food from cans without labels shall not be used;

b) Foods shall be inspected daily for spoilage or signs of mold, and foods that are spoiled or moldy shall be discarded;

c) Meat shall be from government-inspected sources or otherwise approved by the governing health authority;

d) All dairy products shall be pasteurized and Grade A where applicable;

e) Raw, unpasteurized milk, milk products; unpasteurized fruit juices; and raw or undercooked eggs shall not be used. Freshly squeezed fruit or vegetable juice prepared in the child care facility prepared just prior to serving is permissible;

f) Unless a child's health provider documents a different milk product, children from 12 months to 2 years of age shall be served only whole milk. Children older than 2 years of age shall be served whole, skim, 1%, or 2% milk. If allowed by funding resources, dry milk and milk products may be reconstituted in the facility for cooking purposes only, provided that they are prepared, refrigerated, and stored in a sanitary manner, labeled with the date of preparation, and used or discarded within 24 hours of preparation;

g) Meat, fish, poultry, milk, and egg products shall be refrigerated or frozen until immediately before use;

h) Frozen foods shall be defrosted in the refrigerator, under cold running water, as part of the cooking process, or by using the defrost setting of a microwave oven;

i) All fruits and vegetables shall be washed thoroughly with water prior to use;

j) Frozen foods shall never be defrosted by leaving them at room temperature or standing in water that is not kept at refrigerator temperature.

k) Food shall be served promptly after preparation or cooking or maintained at temperatures of not less than 140 degrees F for hot foods and not more than 40 degrees F for cold foods.

l) All opened moist foods that have not been served shall be dated, covered, and maintained at a temperature of 40 degrees F or lower in the refrigerator or 0 degrees F or lower in the freezer, verified by a working thermometer kept in the refrigerator or freezer.

Rationale, comments and references for each Standard are located in *Caring for Our Children, 2nd Edition* (http://nrc.uchsc.edu/CFOC/index.html)

m) Fully cooked and ready-to-serve hot foods shall be held for no longer than 30 minutes before being served, or covered and refrigerated.

## STANDARD 4.058
## SUPPLY OF FOOD AND WATER FOR DISASTERS

In areas where natural disasters (such as earthquakes) occur, a 48 hour supply of food and water shall be kept in stock for each child and staff member.

TYPE OF FACILITY: *Center; Large Family Child Care Home; Small Family Child Care Home*

## STANDARD 4.060
## STORAGE OF CLEANING AGENTS SEPARATE FROM FOOD

Cleaning agents that must be stored in the same room with food shall be clearly labeled and kept separate from food items in locked cabinets. Cleaning agents shall not be stored on shelves above those holding food items. Cleaning agents and food items shall not be stored on the same shelf. Any storage room or cabinet that contains cleaning agents shall be locked. Poisonous or toxic materials shall remain in their original labeled containers.

TYPE OF FACILITY: *Center; Large Family Child Care Home; Small Family Child Care Home*

# CHAPTER 5 - FACILITIES, SUPPLIES, EQUIPMENT, AND TRANSPORTATION

## STANDARD 5.002
## INSPECTION OF BUILDINGS

Newly constructed, renovated, remodeled, or altered buildings shall be inspected by a public inspector to assure compliance with applicable building and fire codes before the building can be made accessible to children.

TYPE OF FACILITY: *Center*

## STANDARD 5.003
## COMPLIANCE WITH FIRE PREVENTION CODE

Every 12 months, the child care facility shall obtain written documentation to submit to the regulatory licensing authority that the facility complies with a state-approved or nationally recognized Fire Prevention Code. If available, this documentation shall be obtained from a fire prevention official with jurisdiction where the facility is located. Where fire safety inspections or a Fire Prevention Code applicable to child care centers is not available from local authorities, the facility shall arrange for a fire safety inspection by an inspector who is recognized by the National Fire Protection Association (NFPA) and is qualified to conduct such inspections using the *NFPA-101 Life Safety Code*.

TYPE OF FACILITY: *Center*

## STANDARD 5.004
## ACCESSIBILITY OF FACILITY

The facility shall be accessible for children who use wheel chairs and for other children and adults with motor disabilities, in accordance with Section 504 of the Rehabilitation Act of 1973 and the Americans with Disabilities Act (ADA). Accessibility includes access to buildings, toilets, sinks, drinking fountains, outdoor play areas, and all classroom and therapy areas. Special provisions shall also be made, as needed, for the child with health, vision, or hearing impairment.

Rationale, comments and references for each Standard are located in *Caring for Our Children, 2nd Edition* (http://nrc.uchsc.edu/CFOC/index.html)

TYPE OF FACILITY: *Center; Large Family Child Care Home; Small Family Child Care Home*

## STANDARD 5.005
## SITE LOCATION FREE FROM HAZARDS

Facilities shall be located on a well-drained site, free from hazards, in areas protected from:
a)   High air pollution;
b)   Loud or constant noises;
c)   Heavy traffic;
d)   Unsafe buildings;
e)   Deep excavations;
f)   Radiation hazards;
g)   Radon hazards;
h)   Pits, abandoned wells or other risks of entrapment or inhumation (burial);
i)   Any other unsafe or harmful environmental elements.

*Editor's Note: See also Standards 5.185 (in CFOC, 2nd Ed.) and 5.186 regarding entrapment hazards.*

TYPE OF FACILITY: *Center; Large Family Child Care Home; Small Family Child Care Home*

## STANDARD 5.014
## POSSIBILITY OF EXIT FROM WINDOWS

All windows in areas used by children under 5 years of age shall be constructed, adapted, or adjusted to limit the exit opening accessible to children to less than 3.5 inches, or be otherwise protected with guards that prevent exit by a child, but that do not block outdoor light. Where such windows are required by building or fire codes to provide for emergency rescue and escape, the windows and guards, if provided, shall be equipped to enable staff to release the guard and open the window fully when escape or rescue is required. Such release shall not require the use of tools or keys.

TYPE OF FACILITY: *Center; Large Family Child Care Home; Small Family Child Care Home*

## STANDARD 5.017
## FINGER-PINCH PROTECTION DEVICES

Finger-pinch protection devices shall be installed wherever doors are accessible to children. These devices include:

a) Rubber gaskets designed to fit into an inset on the door where the door meets the door jamb and over the opening where the door is hinged;
b) Other types of flexible coverings for the hinged opening;
c) Door closing devices that force the door to close slowly or keep the door from closing fully if it strikes an obstacle.

TYPE OF FACILITY: *Center; Large Family Child Care Home; Small Family Child Care Home*

## STANDARD 5.020
## ALTERNATE EXITS AND EMERGENCY SHELTER

Each building or structure, new or old, shall be provided with a minimum of two exits, at different sides of the building or home, leading to an open space at ground level. If the basement in a small family child care home is being used, one exit must lead directly to the outside. Exits shall be unobstructed, allowing occupants to escape to an outside door or exit stair enclosure in case of fire or other emergency. Each floor above or below ground level used for child care shall have at least two unobstructed exits that lead to an open area at ground level and thereafter to an area that meets safety requirements for a child care indoor or outdoor area where children may remain until their parents can pick them up, if reentry into the facility is not possible.

Entrance and exit routes shall be reviewed and approved by the applicable fire inspector. Exiting shall meet all the requirements of the current edition of the *NFPA-101 Life Safety Code* from the National Fire Protection Association (NFPA).

TYPE OF FACILITY: *Center; Large Family Child Care Home; Small Family Child Care Home*

## STANDARD 5.021
## EVACUATION OF CHILDREN WITH DISABILITIES

In facilities that include children who have physical disabilities, all exits and steps necessary for evacuation shall have ramps approved by the local building inspector. Children who have ambulatory difficulty, use wheelchairs or other equipment that must be transported with the child (such as an oxygen ventilator) shall be located on the ground floor of the facility or provisions shall be made for efficient emergency evacuation to a safe sheltered area.

TYPE OF FACILITY: *Center; Large Family Child Care Home; Small Family Child Care Home*

## STANDARD 5.022
## PATH OF EGRESS

The minimum width of any path of egress shall be 36 inches. An exception is that doors shall provide a minimum clear width of 32 inches. The width of doors shall accommodate wheelchairs and the needs of individuals with physical disabilities.

Where exits are not immediately accessible from an open floor area, safe and continuous passageways, aisles, or corridors leading to every exit shall be maintained and shall be arranged to provide access for each occupant to at least two exits by separate ways of travel. Passageways and corridors shall be kept free of materials and furniture that would prevent clear access.

TYPE OF FACILITY: *Center*

## STANDARD 5.023
## LOCKS

The facility shall have no lock or fastening device that prevents free escape from the interior. All door hardware in areas that school-age children use shall be within the reach of the children. In centers, only panic hardware (hardware that can be opened by pressure in the direction of travel) or single-action hardware (hardware that allows a door to open either way but keeps it from swinging back past the center point) shall be permitted on exterior doors.

A double-cylinder deadbolt lock which requires a key to unlock from the inside shall not be permitted on any door along the path of egress from any child care area of a large or small family child care home except the exterior door, and then only if the lock is of a key-capturing type and the key is kept hanging near the door.

If emergency exits lead to potentially unsafe areas for children (such as a busy street), alarms or other signaling devices shall be installed on these exit doors to alert the staff in case a child attempts to leave.

TYPE OF FACILITY: *Center; Large Family Child Care Home; Small Family Child Care Home*

## STANDARD 5.024
## LABELED EMERGENCY EXITS

Emergency exits shall be clearly identified and visible at all times during operation of the child care facility. The exits for escape shall be arranged or marked so the path to safety outside is unmistakable.

TYPE OF FACILITY: *Center*

## STANDARD 5.028
## INDOOR TEMPERATURE AND AIR EXCHANGE

A draft-free temperature of 65 degrees F to 75 degrees F shall be maintained at 30% to 50% relative humidity during the winter months. A draft-free temperature of 68 degrees F to 82 degrees F shall be maintained at 30% to 50% humidity during the summer months. All rooms that children use shall be heated, cooled, and ventilated to maintain the required temperatures, humidity, and air exchange and to avoid accumulation of odors and fumes. Air exchange shall be a minimum of 15 cubic feet per minute (or 7.5 liters/second) per person of outdoor air.

TYPE OF FACILITY: *Center; Large Family Child Care Home; Small Family Child Care Home*

## STANDARD 5.030
## ELECTRIC FANS

Electric fans, if used, shall bear the safety certification mark of a recognized testing laboratory, such as UL (Underwriters Laboratories) or ETL (Electrotechnical Laboratory) and be inaccessible to children.

*Editor's Note: ETL has been renamed Intertek Testing Services.*

TYPE OF FACILITY: *Center; Large Family Child Care Home; Small Family Child Care Home*

## STANDARD 5.034
## GAS, OIL OR KEROSENE HEATERS, PORTABLE GAS STOVES AND CHARCOAL GRILLS

Inadequately vented or unvented gas or oil heaters and portable open-flame kerosene space heaters shall be prohibited. Portable gas stoves and charcoal grills shall not be used for space heating or any other indoor purposes.

Heat in units that involve flame shall be vented properly to the outside and shall be supplied with a source of combustion air that meets the manufacturer's installation requirements.

TYPE OF FACILITY: *Center; Large Family Child Care Home; Small Family Child Care Home*

## STANDARD 5.037
## PROTECTIVE SCREEN FOR HEATING EQUIPMENT

A protective screen shall be in place with a stove used for heating, or any heating equipment with high surface temperature located in an occupied area.

TYPE OF FACILITY: *Center; Large Family Child Care Home; Small Family Child Care Home*

## STANDARD 5.038
## FIREPLACES

Fireplaces and fireplace inserts shall be inaccessible to children. Fireplaces shall be properly drafted and the front opening equipped with a secure and stable protective safety screen. The facility shall provide evidence of cleaning the chimney at least once a year, before the heating season, or as frequently as necessary to prevent excessive build-up of burn residues or smoke products in the chimney. If a fireplace is used when children are present, an adult must be in the same room and the children must be within easy reach of the adult.

TYPE OF FACILITY: *Center; Large Family Child Care Home; Small Family Child Care Home*

## STANDARD 5.039
## BARRIERS/GUARDS FOR HEATING UNITS

Heating units, including hot water heating pipes and baseboard heaters with a surface temperature hotter than 110 degrees F, shall be made inaccessible to children by barriers such as guards or other devices.

TYPE OF FACILITY: *Center; Large Family Child Care Home; Small Family Child Care Home*

## STANDARD 5.047
## ELECTRICAL SERVICE

Facilities shall be supplied with electric service. Outlets and fixtures shall be installed and connected to the source of electric energy in a manner that meets the National Electrical Code, as amended by local electrical codes (if any), and as certified by an electrical code inspector.

TYPE OF FACILITY: *Center; Large Family Child Care Home; Small Family Child Care Home*

## STANDARD 5.048
## SAFETY COVERS AND SHOCK PROTECTION
## DEVICES FOR ELECTRICAL OUTLETS

All electrical outlets accessible to children who are not yet of school-age shall have safety covers that are attached to the electrical receptacle by a screw or other means to prevent easy removal by a child. Outlet covers that a child can remove by extraction of a plug from the socket shall not be used. Unless screw-mounted outlet covers are installed to semi-permanently prevent access to the outlet or outlets are of the child-resistant ground-fault circuit-interrupter (GFCI) type, safety covers shall be used that are spring-loaded or have a comparable means to automatically prohibit access to electricity when a plug is removed from the outlet. All newly installed electrical outlets accessible to children shall be protected by GFCI shock protection devices or safety receptacles that require simultaneous contact with both prongs of a plug to access the electricity.

Rationale, comments and references for each Standard are located in *Caring for Our Children, 2nd Edition* (http://nrc.uchsc.edu/CFOC/index.html)

TYPE OF FACILITY: *Center; Large Family Child Care Home; Small Family Child Care Home*

## STANDARD 5.050
## LOCATION OF ELECTRICAL DEVICES NEAR WATER

No electrical device or apparatus accessible to children shall be located so it could be plugged into an electrical outlet while a person is in contact with a water source, such as a sink, tub, shower area, or swimming/wading pool.

TYPE OF FACILITY: *Center; Large Family Child Care Home; Small Family Child Care Home*

## STANDARD 5.053
## SMOKE DETECTION SYSTEMS

In centers with new installations, a smoke detection system (such as hard-wired system detectors with control panel) shall be installed with placement of the smoke detectors in the following areas:
a) Each story in front of doors to the stairway;
b) Corridors of all floors;
c) Lounges and recreation areas;
d) Sleeping rooms.

In large and small family child care homes, smoke alarms that receive their operating power from the building electrical system shall be installed. Battery-operated smoke alarms shall be permitted provided that the facility demonstrates to the fire inspector that testing, maintenance, and battery replacement programs ensure reliability of power to the smoke alarms and that retrofitting the facility to connect the smoke alarms to the electrical system would be costly and difficult to achieve.

TYPE OF FACILITY: *Center; Large Family Child Care Home; Small Family Child Care Home*

## STANDARD 5.055
## WATER SUPPLY

Every facility shall be supplied with piped running water under pressure, from a source approved by the Environmental Protection Agency (EPA) and/or the regulatory health authority, to provide an adequate water supply to every fixture connected to the water supply and drainage system. The water shall be sufficient in quantity and pressure to supply water for cooking, cleaning, drinking, toilets, and outside uses.

When water is supplied by a well or other private source, it shall meet all applicable federal, state, and local public health standards and shall be approved by the regulatory health authority. Any facility not served by a public water supply shall keep on file documentation of approval of the water supply.

TYPE OF FACILITY: *Center; Large Family Child Care Home; Small Family Child Care Home*

## STANDARD 5.057
## CROSS-CONNECTIONS

The facility shall have no cross-connections that could permit contamination of the potable water supply:
a)  Backflow preventers, vacuum breakers, or strategic air gaps shall be provided for all boiler units in which chemicals are used. Backflow preventers shall be tested annually;
b)  Vacuum breakers shall be installed on all threaded janitorial sink faucets and outdoor/indoor hose bibs;
c)  Nonsubmersible, antisiphon ballcocks shall be provided on all flush tank-type toilets.

TYPE OF FACILITY: *Center; Large Family Child Care Home; Small Family Child Care Home*

## STANDARD 5.060
## HANDWASHING SINK USING PORTABLE WATER SUPPLY

When plumbing is unavailable to provide a handwashing sink, the facility shall provide a handwashing sink using a portable water supply and a sanitary catch system approved by a local public health department. A mechanism shall be in place to prevent children from gaining access to soiled water or more than one child from washing in the same water.

TYPE OF FACILITY: *Center; Large Family Child Care Home; Small Family Child Care Home*

Rationale, comments and references for each Standard are located in *Caring for Our Children, 2nd Edition* (http://nrc.uchsc.edu/CFOC/index.html)

## STANDARD 5.061
## TESTING FOR LEAD LEVELS IN DRINKING WATER

In both private and public drinking water supplies where interior or service piping or joint seals contain lead or other toxic materials, water shall be evaluated at the beginning of operation and at least every 2 years by the regulatory health authority to determine whether lead levels are safe. The samples shall consist of the first draw of water in the facility after at least a 6-hour lapse in use.

TYPE OF FACILITY: *Center; Large Family Child Care Home; Small Family Child Care Home*

## STANDARD 5.064
## SEWAGE FACILITIES

Sewage facilities shall be provided and inspected in accordance with state and local regulations. Whenever a public sewer is available, the facility shall be connected to it. Where public sewers are not available, a septic tank system or other method approved by the local public health department shall be installed. Raw or treated wastes shall not be discharged on the surface of the ground.
The wastewater or septic system drainage field shall not be located within the outdoor play area of a child care center licensed for 13 or more children, unless the drainage field has been designed by a sanitation engineer with the presence of an outdoor play area in mind and meets the approval of the local health authority.

The exhaust vent from a wastewater or septic system and drainage field shall not be located within the children's outdoor play area.

TYPE OF FACILITY: *Center; Large Family Child Care Home; Small Family Child Care Home*

## STANDARD 5.067
## CONTAINMENT OF SOILED DIAPERS

Soiled diapers shall be stored inside the facility in containers separate from other waste. Washable, plastic-lined, tightly covered receptacles, with a firmly fitting cover that does not require touching with contaminated hands or objects, shall be provided, within arm's reach of diaper changing tables, to store soiled diapers. The container for soiled diapers shall be designed to prevent the user from contaminating any exterior surfaces of the container or the user when inserting the soiled diaper. Soiled diapers do not have to be individually bagged before placing them in the container for soiled diapers. Soiled cloth diapers and soiled clothing that are to be sent home with a parent, however, shall be individually bagged.

The following types of diaper containers shall not be used;
a) Those that require the user's hand to push the diaper through a narrow opening;
b) Those with exterior surfaces that must be touched with the hand;
c) Those with exterior surfaces that are likely to be touched with the soiled diaper while the user is discarding the soiled diaper;
d) Those that have lids with handles.

Separate containers shall be used for disposable diapers, cloth diapers (if used), and soiled clothes and linens. All containers shall be inaccessible to children and shall be tall enough to prevent children reaching into the receptacle or from falling headfirst into containers. The containers shall be placed in an area that children cannot enter without close adult supervision.

TYPE OF FACILITY: *Center; Large Family Child Care Home; Small Family Child Care Home*

## STANDARD 5.068
## LABELING, CLEANING AND DISPOSAL OF WASTE AND DIAPER CONTAINERS

Each waste and diaper container shall be labeled to show its intended contents. These containers shall be cleaned daily to keep them free from build-up of soil and odor. Wastewater from these cleaning operations shall be disposed of by pouring it down a toilet or floor drain. Wastewater shall not be poured onto the ground, into handwashing sinks, laundry sinks, kitchen sinks, or bathtubs.

TYPE OF FACILITY: *Center; Large Family Child Care Home; Small Family Child Care Home*

# STANDARD 5.069
# STORAGE AND DISPOSAL OF INFECTIOUS AND TOXIC WASTES

Infectious and toxic wastes shall be stored separately from other wastes, and shall be disposed of in a manner approved by the regulatory health authority.

TYPE OF FACILITY: *Center; Large Family Child Care Home; Small Family Child Care Home*

# STANDARD 5.070
# CONTROL OF ANIMAL WASTE AND PESTS

Areas where children play shall be kept free of animal wastes, insects, infestation by rodents and other pests, and shall not provide shelter to pests.

Whenever the regulatory agency determines that the presence of pests in the area constitutes a health hazard, the facility shall take the necessary actions to exclude, exterminate, or otherwise control such pests on its premises.

All extensive extermination shall be provided by a licensed or certified pest control operator, and only after integrated pest management methods have been exhausted.

TYPE OF FACILITY: *Center; Large Family Child Care Home; Small Family Child Care Home*

# STANDARD 5.073
# TYPE AND USE OF PESTICIDES AND HERBICIDES

If pesticides are used, natural pesticides that are non-toxic to humans shall be given first consideration.

If chemical pesticides are used, they shall be only those that are registered with the Environmental Protection Agency (EPA), of a type applied by a licensed exterminator, in a manner approved by the EPA. The facility shall have and consult a Material Safety Data Sheet (MSDS) for all toxic chemicals used, and shall be in compliance with the directions provided. General right-of-way pesticides or herbicides, sprayed in the community by others, shall be prohibited on the grounds of a child care facility.

Pesticides shall be stored in their original containers and in a locked room or cabinet accessible only to authorized staff. No restricted-use pesticides shall be stored or used on the premises except by properly licensed persons. Banned pesticides shall not be used.

Pesticides shall be applied in a manner that prevents skin contact and other exposure to children or staff members and minimizes odors in occupied areas.

Notification shall be given to parents and staff before using pesticides, to determine if any child or staff member is sensitive to the product. A member of the child care staff shall directly observe the application to be sure that toxic chemicals applied on surfaces do not constitute a hazard to the children or staff. Pesticides shall be used in strict compliance with the instructions on the label or as otherwise directed or approved by the regulatory authority. No pesticide shall be applied while children are present.

Following the use of pesticides, herbicides, fungicides, or other potentially toxic chemicals, the treated area shall be ventilated for the period recommended on the product label or by a nationally certified regional poison control center before being reoccupied. Tests, recommended by a nationally certified regional poison control center, shall be taken to determine safe levels before reentering the facility.

TYPE OF FACILITY: *Center; Large Family Child Care Home; Small Family Child Care Home*

# STANDARD 5.075
## SAFETY OF EQUIPMENT, MATERIALS AND FURNISHINGS

Equipment, materials, furnishings, and play areas shall be sturdy, safe, and in good repair and shall meet the recommendations of the U.S. Consumer Product Safety Commission (CPSC) for control of the following safety hazards:
a) Openings that could entrap a child's head or limbs;
b) Elevated surfaces that are inadequately guarded;
c) Lack of specified surfacing and fall zones under and around climbable equipment;
d) Mismatched size and design of equipment for the intended users;
e) Insufficient spacing between equipment;

Rationale, comments and references for each Standard are located in *Caring for Our Children, 2nd Edition* (http://nrc.uchsc.edu/CFOC/index.html)

f)   Tripping hazards;
g)   Components that can pinch, sheer, or crush body tissues;
h)   Equipment that is known to be of a hazardous type (such as large animal swings);
i)   Sharp points or corners;
j)   Splinters;
k)   Protruding nails, bolts, or other components that could entangle clothing or snag skin;
l)   Loose, rusty parts;
m)  Hazardous small parts that may become detached during normal use or reasonably foreseeable abuse of the equipment and that present a choking, aspiration, or ingestion hazard to a child;
n)   Flaking paint;
o)   Paint that contains lead or other hazardous materials.

TYPE OF FACILITY: *Center; Large Family Child Care Home; Small Family Child Care Home*

## STANDARD 5.083
## BABY WALKERS

Baby walkers that the child can move across the floor shall not be used in any type of child care facility.

TYPE OF FACILITY: *Center; Large Family Child Care Home; Small Family Child Care Home*

## STANDARD 5.084
## AVAILABILITY OF A TELEPHONE

The facility shall provide at least one working non-pay telephone for general and emergency use.

TYPE OF FACILITY: *Center; Large Family Child Care Home; Small Family Child Care Home*

## STANDARD 5.085
## PLAY EQUIPMENT REQUIREMENTS

To provide safety and prevent injury, play equipment and materials in the facility shall meet the recommendations of the U.S. Consumer Product Safety Commission (CPSC) and the American Society for Testing and

Materials (ASTM) for public playground equipment. Equipment and materials intended for *gross-motor* (active) play shall conform to the recommendations in the U.S. CPSC *Handbook for Public Playground Safety* and the provisions in the *ASTM F1487-98 Consumer Safety Performance Specifications for Playground Equipment for Public Use.*

All play equipment shall be constructed, installed, and made available to the intended users in such a manner that meets the American Society for Testing and Materials (ASTM) standards and the U.S. Consumer Product Safety Commission (CPSC) guidelines, as warranted by the manufacturers recommendations. A playground safety inspector who has been certified by the National Recreation and Park Association (NRPA) shall conduct an inspection of playground plans for new installations. Previously installed playgrounds shall be inspected at least once and whenever changes are made to the equipment or intended users.

Play equipment and materials shall be deemed appropriate to the developmental needs, individual interests, and ages of the children, by a person with at least a master's degree in early childhood education or psychology, or a doctoral degree in psychiatry, or identified as age-appropriate by a manufacturer's label on the product package. Enough play equipment and materials shall be available to avoid excessive competition and long waits.

Children shall always be supervised when playing on playground equipment.

> Editor's Note: ASTM Standard F1478-98 has been replaced by ASTM Standard F1487-01e1. Please check ASTM's web site (www.astm.org) for future updates.

TYPE OF FACILITY: *Center; Large Family Child Care Home; Small Family Child Care Home*

## STANDARD 5.087
## INACCESSIBILITY OF TOYS OR OBJECTS TO CHILDREN UNDER 3 YEARS OF AGE

Small objects, toys, and toy parts available to children under the age of 3 years shall meet the federal small parts standards for toys. The following toys or objects shall not be accessible to children under 3 years of age:
a) Toys or objects with removable parts with a diameter less than 1¼ inch and a length less than 2¼ inches;
b) Balls that are smaller than 1¾ inches in diameter;
c) Toys with sharp points and edges;
d) Plastic bags;

Rationale, comments and references for each Standard are located in *Caring for Our Children, 2nd Edition* (http://nrc.uchsc.edu/CFOC/index.html)

e) Styrofoam objects;
f) Coins;
g) Rubber balloons;
h) Safety pins;
i) Marbles;
j) Other small objects.

TYPE OF FACILITY: *Center; Large Family Child Care Home; Small Family Child Care Home*

## STANDARD 5.089
## BALLOONS

Infants, toddlers, and preschool children shall not be permitted to inflate balloons, suck on or put balloons in their mouths nor have access to uninflated or underinflated balloons. Latex balloons or inflated latex objects that are treated as balloons shall not be permitted in the child care facility.

TYPE OF FACILITY: *Center; Large Family Child Care Home; Small Family Child Care Home*

## STANDARD 5.093
## FIRST AID KITS

The facility shall maintain at least one readily available first aid kit wherever children are in care, including one for field trips and outings away from the facility and one to remain at the facility if all the children do not attend the field trip. In addition, a first aid kit shall be in each vehicle that is used to transport children to and from a child care center. Each kit shall be a closed container for storing first aid supplies, accessible to child care staff members at all times but out of reach of children. First aid kits shall be restocked after use, and an inventory shall be conducted at least monthly. The first aid kit shall contain at least the following items:
a) Disposable nonporous gloves;
b) Scissors;
c) Tweezers;
d) A non-glass thermometer to measure a child's temperature;
e) Bandage tape;
f) Sterile gauze pads;
g) Flexible roller gauze;
h) Triangular bandages;

i)   Safety pins;
j)   Eye dressing;
k)   Pen/pencil and note pad;
l)   Syrup of ipecac (use only if recommended by the Poison Control Center);
m)  Cold pack;
n)   Current American Academy of Pediatrics (AAP) standard first aid chart or equivalent first aid guide;
o)   Coins for use in a pay phone;
p)   Water;
q)   Small plastic or metal splints;
r)   Liquid soap;
s)   Adhesive strip bandages, plastic bags for cloths, gauze, and other materials used in handling blood;
t)   Any emergency medication needed for child with special needs;
u)   List of emergency phone numbers, parents' home and work phone numbers, and the Poison Control Center phone number.

TYPE OF FACILITY: *Center; Large Family Child Care Home; Small Family Child Care Home*

# STANDARD 5.100
# USE AND STORAGE OF TOXIC SUBSTANCES

The following items shall be used as recommended by the manufacturer and shall be stored in the original labeled containers:
a)   Cleaning materials;
b)   Detergents;
c)   Automatic dishwasher detergents;
d)   Aerosol cans;
e)   Pesticides;
f)   Health and beauty aids;
g)   Medications;
h)   Lawn care chemicals;
i)   Other toxic materials.

They shall be used only in a manner that will not contaminate play surfaces, food, or food preparation areas, and that will not constitute a hazard to the children. All chemicals used inside or outside shall be stored in their original containers in a safe and secure manner, well away from food. These chemicals shall be used according to manufacturers' instructions, and in a manner that will not contaminate play surfaces or articles.

Rationale, comments and references for each Standard are located in *Caring for Our Children, 2nd Edition* (http://nrc.uchsc.edu/CFOC/index.html)

When not in actual use, toxic materials shall be kept in a locked room or cabinet, fitted with a child-resistive opening device, inaccessible to children, separate from stored medications and food.

Chemicals used in lawn care treatments shall be limited to those listed for use in areas that can be occupied by children.

TYPE OF FACILITY: *Center; Large Family Child Care Home; Small Family Child Care Home*

## STANDARD 5.101
## USE OF A POISON CONTROL CENTER

The poison control center shall be called for advice about any exposure to toxic substances, or any ingestion emergency. The advice shall be followed and documented in the facility's files. The caregiver shall tell the poison information specialist and/or physician the following information:
a)  The child's age and sex;
b)  The substance involved;
c)  The estimated amount;
d)  The child's condition;
e)  The time elapsed since ingestion or exposure.
The caregiver shall not induce vomiting unless instructed by the Poison Control Center.

TYPE OF FACILITY: *Center; Large Family Child Care Home; Small Family Child Care Home*

## STANDARD 5.102
## INFORMING STAFF REGARDING PRESENCE OF TOXIC SUBSTANCES

Employers shall provide child care workers with hazard information, as required by the Occupational Safety and Health Administration (OSHA), about the presence of toxic substances such as asbestos, formaldehyde, or hazardous chemicals in use in the facility. This information shall include identification of the ingredients of art materials and sanitizing products. Where nontoxic substitutes are available, these nontoxic substitutes shall be used instead of toxic chemicals.

TYPE OF FACILITY: *Center; Large Family Child Care Home*

## STANDARD 5.104
## PREVENTING EXPOSURE TO ASBESTOS OR OTHER FRIABLE MATERIALS

Any asbestos, fiberglass, or other friable material or any material that is in a dangerous condition found within a facility or on the grounds of the facility shall be removed. Asbestos removal shall be done by a contractor certified to remove, encapsulate, or enclose asbestos in accordance with existing regulations of the Environmental Protection Agency (EPA). No children shall be present until the removal and cleanup of the hazardous condition have been completed.

Pipe and boiler insulation shall be sampled and examined in an accredited laboratory for the presence of asbestos in a friable or potentially dangerous condition.

Nonfriable asbestos shall be identified to prevent disturbance and/or exposure during remodeling or future activities.

TYPE OF FACILITY: *Center; Large Family Child Care Home; Small Family Child Care Home*

## STANDARD 5.106
## PROHIBITION OF POISONOUS SUBSTANCES AND PLANTS

Poisonous or potentially harmful substances and plants shall be prohibited in any part of a child care facility that is accessible to children. All substances not known to be nontoxic shall be identified and checked by name with the local poison control center to determine safe use.

TYPE OF FACILITY: *Center; Large Family Child Care Home: Small Family Child Care Home*

## STANDARD 5.110
## TESTING FOR LEAD

Any surface and the grounds around and under surfaces that children use at a child care facility, including dirt and grassy areas shall be tested for excessive lead in a location designated by the health department. Painted play equipment and imported vinyl mini-blinds shall be evaluated for the presence of lead. If they are found to have toxic levels, corrective action

Rationale, comments and references for each Standard are located in *Caring for Our Children, 2nd Edition* (http://nrc.uchsc.edu/CFOC/index.html)

shall be taken to prevent exposure to lead at this facility. Only nontoxic paints shall be used.

In all centers, both exterior and interior surfaces covered by paint with lead levels of 0.06% and above, and accessible to children, shall be removed by a safe chemical or physical means or made inaccessible to children, regardless of the condition of the surface.

In large and small family child care homes, flaking or deteriorating lead-based paint on interior or exterior surfaces, equipment, or toys accessible to preschool-age children shall be removed or abated according to health department regulations. Where lead paint is removed, the surface shall be refinished with lead-free paint or nontoxic material. Sanding, scraping, or burning of high-lead surfaces shall be prohibited. Children and pregnant women shall not be present during abatement activities.

TYPE OF FACILITY: *Center; Large Family Child Care Home; Small Family Child Care Home*

## STANDARD 5.111
## CONSTRUCTION AND REMODELING DURING HOURS OF OPERATION

Construction, remodeling, or alterations of structures during child care operations shall be isolated from areas where children are present and done in a manner that will prevent hazards or unsafe conditions (such as fumes, dust, and safety hazards).

TYPE OF FACILITY: *Center; Large Family Child Care Home; Small Family Child Care Home*

## STANDARD 5.112
## SPACE REQUIRED PER CHILD

In general, the designated area for children's activities shall contain a minimum of 35 square feet of usable floor space per child (or compensating for typical furnishings and equipment being present, 50 square feet measured on the inside, wall-to-wall dimensions). In addition, the following shall apply when the indicated, specific types of children are in care:

a) For children with special needs who are 2 to 12 years of age, the minimum usable floor space in a classroom or playroom shall be 40 square feet;

b) When play and sleep areas for infants, toddlers, or preschool-age children are in the same room, a minimum of 35 square feet of usable floor space per child shall be provided except during periods when the children are using their rest equipment. During sleep periods, the space shall be sufficient to provide spacing between children using rest equipment, according to STANDARD 5.142 through STANDARD 5.144.

These spaces are exclusive of food preparation areas of the kitchen, bathrooms, toilets, areas for the care of ill children, offices, staff rooms, corridors, hallways, stairways, closets, lockers, laundry, furnace rooms, cabinets, and storage shelving spaces.

TYPE OF FACILITY: *Center; Large Family Child Care Home; Small Family Child Care Home*

## STANDARD 5.117
## LOCATION OF TOILETS

Toilets shall be located in rooms separate from those used for cooking or eating. If toilets are not on the same floor as the child care area and within sight or hearing of a caregiver, an adult shall accompany children younger than 5 years of age to and from the toilet area.

TYPE OF FACILITY: *Center; Large Family Child Care Home; Small Family Child Care Home*

## STANDARD 5.126
## HANDWASHING SINKS

A handwashing sink shall be accessible without barriers (such as doors) to each child care area. In areas for infants, toddlers, and preschoolers, the sink shall be located so the caregiver may visually supervise the group of children while carrying out routine handwashing or having children wash their hands. Sinks shall be placed at the child's height or be equipped with a stable step platform to make the sink available to children. If a platform is used, it shall have slip-proof steps and platform surface. Also, each sink shall be equipped so that the user has access to:

a) Water, at a temperature at least 60 and no hotter than 120 degrees F;

b) A foot-pedal operated, electric-eye operated, open, self-closing, slow-closing, or metering faucet that provides a flow of water for at least 30 seconds without the need to reactivate the faucet;

c) A supply of handcleansing liquid soap;

d) Disposable single-use cloth or paper towels or a heated-air hand-drying device with heat guards to prevent contact with surfaces that get hotter than 110 degrees F.

A steam tap or a water tap that provides hot water that is hotter than 120 degrees F may not be used at a handwashing sink.

TYPE OF FACILITY: *Center*

## STANDARD 5.129
## DIAPER CHANGING TABLES

The facility shall have at least one diaper changing table per infant group or toddler group to allow sufficient time for changing diapers and for cleaning and sanitizing between children. Diaper changing tables and sinks shall be used only by the children in the group whose routine care is provided together throughout their time in child care. The facility shall not permit shared use of diaper changing tables and sinks by more than one group.

TYPE OF FACILITY: *Center; Large Family Child Care Home*

## STANDARD 5.132
## LOCATION AND SETUP OF DIAPER CHANGING AREAS

The changing area shall not be located in food preparation areas and shall not be used for temporary placement of food or utensils or for serving of food. Food and drinking utensils shall not be washed in these sinks. Changing areas and food preparation areas shall be physically separated.

The diaper changing area shall be set up so that no other surface or supply container is contaminated during diaper changing. Bulk supplies shall not be stored on or brought to the diaper changing surface. Instead, the diapers, wipes, gloves, a thick layer of diaper cream on a piece of disposable paper, a plastic bag for soiled clothes, and disposable paper to cover the table in the amount needed for a specific diaper change will be removed from the bulk container or storage location and placed on or near the diaper changing surface before bringing the child to the diaper changing area.

Conveniently located, washable, plastic lined, tightly covered, hands free receptacles, shall be provided for soiled cloths and linen containing body fluids.

Where only one staff member is available to supervise a group of children, the diaper changing table shall be positioned to allow the staff member to maintain constant sight and sound supervision of children.

TYPE OF FACILITY: *Center; Large Family Child Care Home; Small Family Child Care Home*

## STANDARD 5.145
## CRIBS

Cribs shall be made of wood, metal, or plastic and shall have secure latching devices. They shall have slats spaced no more than 2-3/8 inches apart, with a mattress fitted so that no more than two fingers can fit between the mattress and the crib side in the lowest position. The minimum height from the top of the mattress to the top of the crib rail shall be 20 inches in the highest position. Drop-side latches shall securely hold sides in the raised position, and the child in the crib shall not be able to reach them. Cribs shall not be used with the drop side down. The crib shall not have cornerpost extensions (over 1/16 inch). The crib shall have no cutout openings in the head board or footboard structure in which a child's head could become entrapped. The mattress support system shall not be easily dislodged from any point of the crib by an upward force from underneath the crib. All crib hardware shall be securely tightened and checked regularly. All cribs shall meet the American Society for Testing Materials (ASTM) *F1169-99 Standard Specification for Full Size Baby Crib, F966-00 Standard Consumer Safety Specifications for Full-Size and Non-Full-Size Baby Crib Corner Post Extensions,* and the Code of Federal Regulations *16 CFR 1508 Requirements for Full-Size Baby Cribs and 16 CFR 1509 Requirements for Non-Full-Size Baby Cribs.*

*Editor's Note: ASTM's standard for non-full-size cribs is: F406-02 Consumer Safety Specification for Non-Full-Size Cribs/Play Yards*

TYPE OF FACILITY: *Center; Large Family Child Care Home; Small Family Child Care Home*

## STANDARD 5.146
## INFANT SLEEPING POSITION EQUIPMENT AND SUPPLIES

Infants under 12 months of age shall be placed on their backs on a firm mattress, mat or pad manufactured for sale in the United States as infant sleeping equipment, for sleep. The mattress, mat, or pad shall either be tightly fitted in furniture manufactured for sale in the United States as infant sleeping equipment or placed where the child cannot fall to a lower surface while resting. If no containing structure is used, the child shall be protected from access to hazards in the sleeping area. Waterbeds, sofas, soft mattresses, pillows, and other soft surfaces shall be prohibited as infant sleeping surfaces. All pillows, quilts, comforters, sheepskins, stuffed toys, and other soft products shall be removed from the crib. If a blanket is used, the infant shall be placed at the foot of the crib with a thin blanket tucked around the crib mattress, reaching only as far as the infant's chest. The infant's head shall remain uncovered during sleep.

TYPE OF FACILITY: *Center; Large Family Child Care Home; Small Family Child Care Home*

## STANDARD 5.157
## INACCESSIBILITY MATCHES AND LIGHTERS

Matches and lighters shall not be accessible to children.

TYPE OF FACILITY: *Center; Large Family Child Care Home; Small Family Child Care Home*

## STANDARD 5.158
## STORAGE OF FLAMMABLE MATERIALS

Gasoline and other flammable materials shall be stored in a separate building, away from the children.

TYPE OF FACILITY: *Center; Large Family Child Care Home; Small Family Child Care Home*

## STANDARD 5.159
## STORAGE OF PLASTIC BAGS

Plastic bags, whether intended for storage, trash, diaper disposal, or any other purpose, shall be stored out of reach of children.

TYPE OF FACILITY: *Center; Large Family Child Care Home; Small Family Child Care Home*

## STANDARD 5.160
## INACCESSIBILITY OF STRINGS AND CORDS

Strings and cords (such as those that are parts of toys and those found on window coverings) long enough to encircle a child's neck shall not be accessible to children in child care.

Pacifiers attached to strings or ribbons shall not be placed around infants' necks or attached to infants' clothing.

Hood and neck strings from all children's outerwear, including jackets and sweatshirts, shall be removed. Drawstrings on the waist or bottom of garments shall not extend more than 3 inches outside the garment when it is fully expanded. These strings shall have no knots or toggles on the free ends. The drawstring shall be sewn to the garment at its midpoint so the string cannot be pulled out through one side.

TYPE OF FACILITY: *Center; Large Family Child Care Home; Small Family Child Care Home*

## STANDARD 5.161
## FIREARMS

Centers shall not have any firearms, pellet or BB guns (loaded or unloaded), darts, bows and arrows, cap pistols, or objects manufactured for play as toy guns within the premises at any time. If present in a small or large family child care home, these items must be unloaded, equipped with child protective devices, and kept under lock and key in areas inaccessible to the children. Parents shall be informed about this policy.

TYPE OF FACILITY: *Center; Large Family Child Care Home; Small Family Child Care Home*

## STANDARD 5.165
## ROOFTOPS AS PLAY AREAS

A rooftop used as a play area shall be enclosed with a fence not less than 6 feet high, and the bottom edge shall be no more than 3 ½ inches from the base. The fence shall be designed to prevent children from climbing it. An approved fire escape shall lead from the roof to an open space at the ground level that meets the safety standards for outdoor play areas.

TYPE OF FACILITY: *Center*

## STANDARD 5.166
## ELEVATED PLAY AREAS

Elevated play areas that have been created using a retaining wall shall have a guardrail or fence running along the top of the retaining wall.

If the exposed side of the retaining wall is higher than 2 feet, a fence not less than 6 feet high shall be installed. The bottom edge of the fence shall be no more than 3 ½ inches from the base. The fence shall be designed

to prevent children from climbing it. If the height of the exposed side of the retaining wall is 2 feet or lower, a guardrail shall be installed.

TYPE OF FACILITY: *Center; Large Family Child Care Home; Small Family Child Care Home*

## STANDARD 5.167
## LOCATION OF SATELLITE DISHES

A satellite dish shall not be located within playgrounds or other areas accessible to children. If a satellite dish is on the premises, it shall be surrounded by a fence or natural barrier (at least 4 feet high) to prevent children from climbing on it.

TYPE OF FACILITY: *Center; Large Family Child Care Home; Small Family Child Care Home*

## STANDARD 5.173
## SHADING OF METAL OUTDOOR PLAY EQUIPMENT

Metal equipment (especially slides) shall be placed in the shade.

TYPE OF FACILITY: *Center; Large Family Child Care Home; Small Family Child Care Home*

## STANDARD 5.179
## HAZARDOUS CHEMICALS IN THE SOIL OF PLAY AREAS

The soil in play areas shall not contain hazardous levels of any toxic chemical or substance. Where there is reason to believe a problem may exist, the facility shall have soil samples analyzed by an agency responsible for soil testing, or by a soil testing laboratory recommended by the regulatory health agency.

The soil in play areas shall be analyzed for lead content initially and shall be analyzed at least once every 2 years where the exteriors of adjacent buildings and structures are painted with lead-containing paint. Lead in soil shall not exceed 500 ppm (parts per million). Testing and analyses shall be in accordance with procedures specified by the regulating health authority.

*Editor's Note: EPA's current recommendation is lead in soil shall not exceed 400 ppm (parts per million).*

TYPE OF FACILITY: *Center; Large Family Child Care Home; Small Family Child Care Home*

## STANDARD 5.183
## PROHIBITED SURFACES FOR PLACING CLIMBING EQUIPMENT

Equipment used for climbing shall not be placed over, or immediately next to, hard surfaces such as asphalt, concrete, dirt, grass, or flooring covered by carpet or gym mats not intended for use as surfacing for climbing equipment.

All pieces of playground equipment shall be surrounded by a shock-absorbing surface. This material may be either the unitary or the loose-fill type, as defined by the guidelines of the U.S. Consumer Product Safety

Commission (CPSC) and the standard of the American Society for Testing and Materials (ASTM), extending at least 6 feet beyond the perimeter of the stationary equipment. These shock-absorbing surfaces must conform to the standard stating that the impact of falling from the height of the structure will be less than or equal to peak deceleration 200G and a Head Injury Criterion (HIC) of 1000. Organic materials that support colonization of molds and bacteria shall not be used. This standard applies whether the equipment is installed outdoors or indoors.

TYPE OF FACILITY: *Center; Large Family Child Care Home; Small Family Child Care Home*

## STANDARD 5.184
## ENCLOSURE OF MOVING PARTS ON PLAY EQUIPMENT

All pieces of play equipment shall be designed so moving parts (swing components, teeter-totter mechanism, spring-ride springs, and so forth) will be shielded or enclosed.

*Editor's Note: See also Standard 5.185 (in CFOC, 2nd Ed.) regarding pinch, crush and shear points.*

TYPE OF FACILITY: *Center; Large Family Child Care Home; Small Family Child Care Home*

## STANDARD 5.186
## ENTRAPMENT HAZARDS OF PLAY EQUIPMENT

All pieces of play equipment shall be designed to guard against entrapment or situations that may cause strangulation by being too large for a child's head to get stuck or too small for a child's head to fit into. Openings in exercise rings shall be smaller than 3½ inches or larger than 9 inches in diameter. A play structure shall have no openings with a dimension between 3½ inches and 9 inches. In particular, side railings, stairs, and other locations where a child might slip or try to climb through shall be checked for appropriate dimensions.

Protrusions such as pipes or wood ends that may catch a child's clothing are prohibited. Distances between two vertical objects that are positioned near each other shall be 3½ inches or less to prevent entrapment of a child's head. No opening shall have a vertical angle of less than 55 degrees. To prevent entrapment of fingers, no openings shall be larger than 3/8 inch or smaller than 1 inch.

*Editor's Note: Readers should periodically check ASTM and CPSC web sites for current updates on their playground equipment standards (www.astm.org and www.cpsc.gov)*

TYPE OF FACILITY: *Center; Large Family Child Care Home; Small Family Child Care Home*

## STANDARD 5.187
## PLAY EQUIPMENT FOR CHILDREN WITH DISABILITIES

Play equipment and play surfaces shall be provided for children with disabilities. Play equipment and play surfaces shall conform to recommendations from the Americans with Disabilities Act (ADA).

TYPE OF FACILITY: *Center; Large Family Child Care Home; Small Family Child Care Home*

## STANDARD 5.194
## REMOVAL OF HAZARDS FROM OUTDOOR AREAS

All outdoor activity areas shall be maintained in a clean and safe condition by removing:
a) Debris;
b) Dilapidated structures;
c) Broken or worn play equipment;
d) Building supplies and equipment;
e) Glass;
f) Sharp rocks;
g) Stumps and roots;
h) Twigs;
i) Toxic plants;
j) Anthills;
k) Beehives and wasp nests;
l) Unprotected ditches;
m) Wells;
n) Holes;
o) Grease traps;
p) Cisterns;
q) Cesspools;

Rationale, comments and references for each Standard are located in *Caring for Our Children, 2nd Edition* (http://nrc.uchsc.edu/CFOC/index.html)

r)   Unprotected utility equipment;
s)   Other injurious material.

Holes or abandoned wells within the site shall be properly filled or sealed. The area shall be well-drained, with no standing water.

A maintenance policy for playgrounds and outdoor areas shall be established and followed.

TYPE OF FACILITY: *Center; Large Family Child Care; Small Family Child Care Home*

## STANDARD 5.195
## TOXIC MATERIALS USED ON OUTDOOR PLAY EQUIPMENT

Outdoor play equipment shall not be coated or treated with, nor shall it contain, toxic materials in hazardous amounts that are accessible to children.

TYPE OF FACILITY: *Center; Large Family Child Care Home; Small Family Child Care Home*

## STANDARD 5.196
## INSPECTION OF PLAY AREA AND EQUIPMENT

The play area and equipment shall be inspected for safety at regular intervals and the observations documented.

Playground equipment shall be checked according to the manufacturer's instructions for the following:
a)   Visible cracks, bending or warping, rusting, or breakage of any equipment;
b)   Deformation of open hooks, shackles, rings, links, and so forth;
c)   Worn swing hangers and chains;
d)   Missing, damaged, or loose swing seats;
e)   Broken supports or anchors;
f)   Cement support footings that are exposed, cracked, or loose in the ground;
g)   Accessible sharp edges or points;
h)   Exposed ends of tubing that require covering with plugs or caps;
i)   Protruding bolt ends that have lost caps or covers;
j)   Loose bolts, nuts, and so forth that require tightening;

k)  Splintered, cracked, or otherwise deteriorating wood;
l)  Lack of lubrication on moving parts;
m)  Worn bearings or other mechanical parts or missing rails, steps, rungs, or seats;
n)  Worn or scattered surfacing material;
o)  Hard surfaces, especially under swings, slides, and so forth (such as places where resilient material has been shifted away from any surface underneath play equipment);
p)  Chipped or peeling paint;
q)  Pinch or crush points, exposed mechanisms, juncture, and moving components.

Outdoor play areas shall be checked daily for areas of poor drainage and accumulation of water and ice.

TYPE OF FACILITY: *Center; Large Family Child Care Home; Small Family Child Care Home*

# STANDARD 5.198
# ENCLOSURE OF BODIES OF WATER

All water hazards, such as pools, swimming pools, stationary wading pools, ditches, and fish ponds, shall be enclosed with a fence that is at least 5 feet high and comes within 3½ inches of the ground. Openings in the fence shall be no greater than 3½ inches. The fence shall be constructed to discourage climbing and kept in good repair.

If the fence is made of horizontal and vertical members (like a typical wooden fence) and the distance between the tops of the horizontal parts of the fence is less than 45 inches, the horizontal parts shall be on the swimming pool side of the fence. The spacing of the vertical members shall not exceed 1¾ inches.

For a chain link fence, the mesh size shall not exceed 1¼ inches square.

Exit and entrance points shall have self-closing, positive latching gates with locking devices a minimum of 55 inches from the ground.

A wall of the child care facility shall not constitute one side of the fence unless the wall has no openings capable of providing direct access to the pool (such as doors, windows, or other openings).

Rationale, comments and references for each Standard are located in *Caring for Our Children, 2nd Edition* (http://nrc.uchsc.edu/CFOC/index.html)

If the facility has a water play area, the following requirements shall be met:
a)   Water play areas shall conform to all state and local health regulations;
b)   Water play areas shall not include hidden or enclosed spaces;
c)   Spray areas and water-collecting areas shall have a non-slip surface, such as asphalt;
d)   Water play areas, particularly those that have standing water, shall not have sudden changes in depth of water;
e)   Drains, streams, water spouts, and hydrants shall not create strong suction effects or water-jet forces;
f)   All toys and other equipment used in and around the water play area shall be made of sturdy plastic or metal. No glass shall be permitted;
g)   Water play areas in which standing water is maintained for more than 24 hours shall be inspected for glass, trash, animal excrement, and other foreign material.

TYPE OF FACILITY: *Center; Large Family Child Care Home; Small Family Child Care Home*

## STANDARD 5.199
## ACCESSIBILITY TO ABOVE-GROUND POOLS

Above-ground pools shall have non-climbable sidewalls that are at least 4 feet high or shall be enclosed with an approved fence, as specified in STANDARD 5.198. When the pool is not in use, steps shall be removed from the pool or otherwise protected to ensure that they cannot be accessed.

*Editor's Note: Correction: walls shall be at least 5 feet high.*

TYPE OF FACILITY: *Center; Large Family Child Care Home; Small Family Child Care Home*

## STANDARD 5.208
## LIFESAVING EQUIPMENT

Each swimming pool more than 6 feet in width, length, or diameter shall be provided with a ring buoy and rope, or a rescue tube, or a throwing line and a shepherd's hook. This equipment shall be long enough to reach the center of the pool from the edge of the pool, shall be kept in good repair, and shall be stored safely and conveniently for immediate access.

TYPE OF FACILITY: *Center; Large Family Child Care Home; Small Family Child Care Home*

## STANDARD 5.209
## LIFELINE IN POOL

A lifeline shall be provided at the 5-foot break in grade between the shallow and deep portions of the swimming pool.

TYPE OF FACILITY: *Center; Large Family Child Care Home; Small Family Child Care Home*

## STANDARD 5.211
## HOT TUBS, SPAS, AND SAUNAS

Children shall not be permitted in hot tubs, spas, or saunas. Areas shall be secured to prevent unsupervised access by children.

TYPE OF FACILITY: *Center; Large Family Child Care Home; Small Family Child Care Home*

## STANDARD 5.217
## CHLORINE PUCKS

"Chlorine Pucks" must not be placed in skimmer baskets.

TYPE OF FACILITY: *Center; Large Family Child Care Home; Small Family Child Care Home*

## STANDARD 5.225
## STAIRWAY GUARDS

Securely installed, effective guards (such as gates) shall be provided at the top and bottom of each open stairway in facilities where infants and toddlers are in care. Gates shall have latching devices that adults (but not children) can open easily in an emergency. "Pressure gates" or accordion gates shall not be used. Basement stairways shall be shut off from the main floor level by a full door. This door shall be self-closing and shall be kept locked to entry when the basement is not in use. No door shall be locked to prohibit exit at any time.

Rationale, comments and references for each Standard are located in *Caring for Our Children, 2nd Edition* (http://nrc.uchsc.edu/CFOC/index.html)

TYPE OF FACILITY: *Center; Large Family Child Care Home; Small Family Child Care Home*

## STANDARD 5.236
## VEHICLE CHILD RESTRAINT SYSTEMS

Age and size appropriate vehicle child restraint systems shall be used for children under 80 pounds and 4 feet 9 inches. Vehicle child restraint systems shall be secured in back seats only. Infants shall ride facing the back of the car until they have reached one year of age and weigh at least 20 pounds. A booster child safety seat shall be used when the child has outgrown a convertible child safety seat but is too small to fit properly in a vehicle safety belt.

All children, who weigh at least 80 pounds and are at least 4 feet 9 inches in height, shall wear seatbelts.

TYPE OF FACILITY: *Center; Large Family Child Care Home; Small Family Child Care Home*

## STANDARD 5.242
## SAFETY HELMETS

All children shall wear approved safety helmets while riding toys with a wheel-base of more than 20 inches in diameter. Approved helmets shall meet the standards of either the U.S. Consumer Product Safety Commission (CPSC), American Society for Testing and Materials (ASTM), or the Snell Memorial Foundation.

*Editor's Note: See also Standard 5.092 (in CFOC, 2nd Ed) regarding other safety measures when using helmets.*

TYPE OF FACILITY: *Center; Large Family Child Care Home; Small Family Child Care Home*

# CHAPTER 6 - INFECTIOUS DISEASES

## STANDARD 6.003
## INFORMING PUBLIC HEALTH AUTHORITIES OF HIB CASES

Local and/or state public health authorities shall be notified immediately about cases of *H. influenzae* type b (Hib) infections involving children or child care providers in the child care setting. Facilities shall cooperate with their health department in notifying parents of children who attend the facility about exposure to children with Hib disease. This may include providing local health officials with the names and telephone numbers of parents of children in classrooms or facilities involved.

The health department may recommend rifampin, an antibiotic taken to prevent infection, for children in care and staff members, to prevent secondary spread of Hib disease in the facility. Antibiotic prophylaxis is not recommended for pregnant women because the effect of rifampin on the fetus has not been established.

TYPE OF FACILITY: *Center; Large Family Child Care Home; Small Family Child Care Home*

## STANDARD 6.004
## IMMUNIZATION WITH *S. PNEUMONIAE* CONJUGATE VACCINE

All children less than 23 months of age in child care shall have received age-appropriate immunizations with *S. pneumoniae* conjugate vaccine. Children age 24 to 59 months of age at high risk of invasive disease caused by *S. pneumoniae* (including sickle cell disease, asplenia, HIV, chronic illness or immunocompromised) shall be recommended to receive *S. pneumoniae* conjugate vaccine. All other children 24-59 months of age shall be encouraged to be protected against invasive *S. pneumoniae* disease through immunization, especially children who attend out-of-home child care and children of American Indian, Alaska Native, and African-American descent.

TYPE OF FACILITY: *Center; Large Family Child Care Home; Small Family Child Care Home*

Rationale, comments and references for each Standard are located in *Caring for Our Children, 2nd Edition* (http://nrc.uchsc.edu/CFOC/index.html)

## STANDARD 6.005
## INFORMING PUBLIC HEALTH AUTHORITIES OF
## INVASIVE *S. PNEUMONIAE*

Local and/or state public health authorities shall be notified immediately about cases of invasive *S. pneumoniae* infections involving children or child care providers in the child care setting. Facilities shall cooperate with their health department in notifying parents of children who attend the facility about exposure to children with invasive *S. pneumoniae* disease. This may include providing local health officials with the names and telephone numbers of parents of children in classrooms or facilities involved.

*Editor's Note: Notification shall occur for cases involving children 5 years of age or less.*

TYPE OF FACILITY: *Center; Large Family Child Care Home; Small Family Child Care Home*

## STANDARD 6.006
## INFORMING PUBLIC HEALTH AUTHORITIES OF
## MENINGOCOCCAL INFECTIONS

Local and/or state public health authorities shall be notified immediately about cases of meningococcal infections involving children or child care providers in the child care setting. Facilities shall cooperate with their local health department officials in notifying parents of children who attend the facility about exposures to children with meningococcal infections. This may include providing local health officials with the names and telephone numbers of parents of children in involved classrooms or facilities.

TYPE OF FACILITY: *Center; Large Family Child Care Home; Small Family Child Care Home*

## STANDARD 6.007
## HEALTH DEPARTMENT RECOMMENDATIONS ON
## ANTIBIOTICS

When the health department recommends administering an antibiotic to prevent secondary infection of meningococcal disease within the facility, an antibiotic to prevent an infection shall be administered to staff members and children, with parental permission.

TYPE OF FACILITY: *Center; Large Family Child Care Home; Small Family Child Care Home*

# STANDARD 6.009
## INFORMING PUBLIC HEALTH AUTHORITIES OF PERTUSSIS CASES

Local and/or state public health authorities shall be notified immediately about cases of pertussis involving children or child care providers in the child care setting. Facilities shall cooperate with their local health department officials in notifying parents of children who attend the facility about exposures to children with pertussis. This may include providing the health department officials with the names and telephone numbers of parents of children in the classrooms or facilities involved.

Guidelines for use of antibiotics and immunization for prevention of pertussis in individuals who have been in contact with children who have pertussis shall be implemented in cooperation with officials of the health department. Children and staff who have been exposed to pertussis, especially those who are incompletely immunized, shall be observed for respiratory tract symptoms for 20 days after the last contact with the infected person.

TYPE OF FACILITY: *Center; Large Family Child Care Home; Small Family Child Care Home*

# STANDARD 6.014
## MEASURES FOR DETECTION AND CONTROL OF TUBERCULOSIS

Local and/or state public health authorities shall be notified immediately about suspected cases of tuberculosis disease involving children or child care providers in the child care setting. Facilities shall cooperate with their local health department officials in notifying parents of children who attend the facility about exposures to children or staff with tuberculosis disease. This may include providing the health department officials with the names and telephone numbers of parents of children in the classrooms or facilities involved.

Tuberculosis transmission shall be controlled by requiring regular and substitute staff members and volunteers to have their tuberculosis status assessed with a one-step or two-step Mantoux intradermal skin test

Rationale, comments and references for each Standard are located in *Caring for Our Children, 2nd Edition* (http://nrc.uchsc.edu/CFOC/index.html)

prior to beginning employment unless they produce documentation of the following:
a)   A positive Mantoux intradermal skin test result in the past, or
b)   Tuberculosis disease that has been treated appropriately in the past.

The one-step Mantoux intradermal tuberculin test shall suffice except that for individuals over 60 years of age or those who have a medical condition that reduces their immune response, the use of the two-step method is required. Individuals with a positive Mantoux intradermal skin test or tuberculosis disease in the past shall be evaluated with chest radiographs and shall be cleared for work by their physician or a health department official. Review of the health status of any staff member with a positive Mantoux intradermal skin test or tuberculosis disease in the past shall be part of the routine annual staff health appraisal.

In large and small family child care homes, this requirement applies to all adolescents and adults who are present while the children are in care.

Tuberculosis screening by Mantoux intradermal skin testing, using the one-step procedure, of staff members with previously negative skin tests shall not be repeated on a regular basis unless required by the local or state health department. Anyone who develops an illness consistent with tuberculosis shall be evaluated promptly by a physician. Staff members with previously positive skin tests shall be under the care of a physician who, annually, will document the risk of contagion related to the person's tuberculosis status by performing a symptom review including asking about chronic cough, unintentional weight, unexplained fever and other potential risk factors.

*Editor's Note: Mantoux intradermal skin test is now referred to as Tuberculin skin test (TST). In the last sentence, it should be unintentional weight "loss". The word "loss" was unintentionally left out.*

TYPE OF FACILITY: *Center; Large Family Child Care Home; Small Family Child Care Home*

## STANDARD 6.015
## ATTENDANCE OF CHILDREN WITH TUBERCULOSIS INFECTION

Children with tuberculosis infection or disease can attend child care if they are receiving appropriate therapy.

TYPE OF FACILITY: *Center; Large Family Child Care Home; Small Family Child Care Home*

## STANDARD 6.016
## ATTENDANCE OF CHILDREN WITH ERYTHEMA INFECTIOSUM (EI)

Children who develop erythema infectiosum (EI), also known as fifth disease, following infection with parvovirus B19, shall be allowed to attend child care because they are no longer contagious when signs and symptoms appear.

TYPE OF FACILITY: *Center; Large Family Child Care Home; Small Family Child Care Home*

## STANDARD 6.018
## DISEASE RECOGNITION AND CONTROL OF HERPES SIMPLEX VIRUS

Children with herpetic gingivostomatitis, an infection of the mouth caused by the herpes simplex virus, who do not have control of oral secretions shall be excluded from child care. In selected situations, children with mild disease who are in control of their mouth secretions may not have to be excluded. The facility's health consultant or health department officials shall be consulted.

Child care providers with herpetic gingivostomatitis, cold sores, or herpes labialis shall do the following:
a) Refrain from kissing and nuzzling children;
b) Refrain from sharing food and drinks with children and other caregivers;
c) Avoid touching the lesions;
d) Wash their hands frequently;
e) Cover any skin lesion with a bandage, clothing, or an appropriate dressing.

Child care providers shall be instructed in the importance of and technique for handwashing and other measures aimed at limiting the transfer of infected material, such as saliva, tissue fluid, or fluid from a skin sore.

TYPE OF FACILITY: *Center; Large Family Child Care Home; Small Family Child Care Home*

Rationale, comments and references for each Standard are located in *Caring for Our Children, 2nd Edition* (http://nrc.uchsc.edu/CFOC/index.html)

## STANDARD 6.021
## STAFF EDUCATION AND POLICIES ON CYTOMEGALOVIRUS (CMV)

Facilities that employ women of childbearing age shall educate these workers with regard to the following:

a) The increased probability of exposure to cytomegalovirus (CMV) in the child care setting;

b) The potential for fetal damage when CMV is acquired during pregnancy;

c) Hygiene measures (especially handwashing and avoiding contact with urine, saliva, and nasal secretions) aimed at reducing the acquisition of CMV;

d) The availability of counseling and testing for serum antibody to CMV to determine the child care provider's immune status.

Female employees of childbearing age shall be referred to their personal health care providers or to the health department authority for counseling about their risk of cytomegalovirus (CMV) infection. This counseling may include testing for serum antibodies to CMV to determine the employee's immunity against CMV infection.

TYPE OF FACILITY: *Center; Large Family Child Care Home; Small Family Child Care Home*

## STANDARD 6.025
## DISEASE SURVEILLANCE OF ENTERIC (DIARRHEAL) AND HAV INFECTIONS

The child care facility shall cooperate with local health authorities in notifying all staff and parents of other children who attend the facility of possible exposure to hepatitis A, and diarrheal agents such as *E. coli: 0157:H7, Shigella,* rotavirus and other enteric viruses, *Salmonella, Campylobacter, Giardia lamblia,* and *Cryptosporidium.*

TYPE OF FACILITY: *Center; Large Family Child Care Home; Small Family Child Care Home*

## STANDARD 6.026
## MAINTENANCE OF RECORDS ON INCIDENTS OF DIARRHEA

The facility shall maintain a record of children and caregivers who have diarrhea while at home or at the facility. This record shall include:
a) The child or caregiver's name;
b) Dates the child or caregiver is ill;
c) Reason for diarrhea, if known;
d) Whether the child or caregiver was in attendance at the child care facility during the diarrhea episode;
e) Any leakage of feces from the diaper while the child was in attendance at the child care facility.

The facility shall notify the local health department authorities whenever there have been two or more children with diarrhea in a given classroom or three or more unrelated children (not siblings) within the facility within a 2-week period.

TYPE OF FACILITY: *Center; Large Family Child Care Home; Small Family Child Care Home*

## STANDARD 6.027
## DISEASE RECOGNITION AND CONTROL OF HBV INFECTION

Facilities shall have written policies for inclusion and exclusion of children known to be infected with hepatitis B virus (HBV) and immunization of children with hepatitis B vaccine as part of their routine immunization schedule. When a child who is an HBV carrier is admitted to a facility, the facility director or the caregiver usually responsible for the child shall be informed.

Children who carry HBV chronically and who have no behavioral or medical risk factors, such as aggressive behavior (biting and frequent scratching), generalized dermatitis (weeping skin lesions), or bleeding problems shall be admitted to the facility without restrictions.

Testing of children for HBV shall not be a prerequisite for admission to facilities.

With regard to infection control measures, every person shall be assumed to be an HBV carrier. Child care personnel shall adopt standard precautions, as outlined in Prevention of Exposure to Blood, STANDARD 3.026 and STANDARD 3.027.

Toys and objects that young children (infants and toddlers) mouth shall be cleaned and sanitized, as stated in STANDARD 3.036 through STANDARD 3.038.

Toothbrushes shall be individually labeled so that the children do not share toothbrushes, as specified in STANDARD 5.095.

> TYPE OF FACILITY: *Center; Large Family Child Care Home; Small Family Child Care Home*

## STANDARD 6.029
## STAFF EDUCATION ON PREVENTION OF BLOODBORNE DISEASES

All caregivers shall receive regular training on how to prevent transmission of bloodborne diseases, including hepatitis B virus (HBV).

> TYPE OF FACILITY: *Center; Large Family Child Care Home; Small Family Child Care Home*

## STANDARD 6.032
## INFECTION CONTROL MEASURES WITH HCV

Standard precautions, as outlined in STANDARD 3.026, shall be followed to prevent infection with hepatitis C virus (HCV) infection. Children with HCV infection shall not be excluded from out-of-home child care.

> TYPE OF FACILITY: *Center; Large Family Child Care Home; Small Family Child Care Home*

## STANDARD 6.034
## PROTECTING HIV-INFECTED CHILDREN AND ADULTS IN CHILD CARE

Parents of all children, including human immunodeficiency virus (HIV) infected children, shall be notified immediately if the child has been exposed to chickenpox, tuberculosis, fifth disease (parvovirus B19), diarrheal disease, measles, or other infectious diseases through other children in the facility.

Children whose immune systems do not function properly to prevent infection and who are exposed to measles or chickenpox shall be referred immediately to their health care provider to receive the appropriate preventive measure (immune globulin or immunization) following exposure and decision about readmission to the child care facility.

Caregivers known to be HIV-infected shall be notified immediately if they have been exposed to chickenpox, fifth disease, tuberculosis, diarrheal disease, or measles through children in the facility. If they have been exposed to measles or chickenpox, they shall receive an appropriate preventive measure (immune globulin or immunization) after exposure. Their return to work after exposure shall be determined jointly by the director of the center (or, in the cases of large family child care homes and small family child care homes, the primary caregiver) and the health care provider for the HIV-infected caregiver.

Information regarding a child whose immune system does not function properly to prevent infection, whatever the cause, shall be available to caregivers who need to know so they can reduce the likelihood of transmission of infection to the child. Accordingly, infections in other children and staff members in the facility shall be brought to the prompt attention of the parent of the child whose immune system does not function properly. The parent may elect to seek medical advice regarding the child's continued participation in the facility. Injuries that lead to bleeding by a child with human immunodeficiency virus (HIV) shall be handled promptly in the manner recommended for any such injury in any child using standard precautions.

TYPE OF FACILITY: *Center; Large Family Child Care Home; Small Family Child Care Home*

## STANDARD 6.035
## STAFF EDUCATION ABOUT PREVENTING TRANSMISSION OF HIV INFECTION

Caregivers shall be knowledgeable about routes of transmission and about prevention of transmission of bloodborne pathogens, including human immunodeficiency virus (HIV) and shall practice measures recommended by the U.S. Public Health Service for prevention of transmission of these infections.

TYPE OF FACILITY: *Center; Large Family Child Care Home; Small Family Child Care Home*

Rationale, comments and references for each Standard are located in *Caring for Our Children, 2nd Edition* (http://nrc.uchsc.edu/CFOC/index.html)

## STANDARD 6.037
## ATTENDANCE OF CHILDREN WITH SCABIES

Children with scabies shall be removed from the child care facility until appropriate treatment has been administered. Children shall be allowed to return to child care after treatment has been completed.

TYPE OF FACILITY: *Center; Large Family Child Care Home; Small Family Child Care Home*

## STANDARD 6.038
## ATTENDANCE OF CHILDREN WITH HEAD LICE

Children shall not be excluded immediately or sent home early from child care because of head lice. Parents of affected children shall be notified and informed that their child must be treated properly before returning to the child care facility the next day.

Children and staff who have been in close contact with an affected child shall be examined and treated if infested. Infestation shall be identified by the presence of adult lice or nits (eggs) on a hair shaft 3 to 4 mm from the scalp.

TYPE OF FACILITY: *Center; Large Family Child Care Home; Small Family Child Care Home*

## STANDARD 6.039
## ATTENDANCE OF CHILDREN WITH RINGWORM

Children with ringworm of the scalp or body shall receive appropriate treatment. Children receiving treatment shall not be excluded from child care.

Children and staff in close contact with an affected child shall receive periodic inspections for early lesions and receive prompt therapy.

TYPE OF FACILITY: *Center; Large Family Child Care Home; Small Family Child Care Home*

# CHAPTER 7 - CHILDREN WHO ARE ELIGIBLE FOR SERVICES UNDER IDEA

## STANDARD 7.005
## FORMULATION OF AN ACTION PLAN

The formulation of an action plan, as determined by the child's needs, shall be based on the assessment process specified in STANDARD 7.003 and STANDARD 7.004. Such a plan shall be written and shall be maintained as part of each child's confidential record.

TYPE OF FACILITY: *Center; Large Family Child Care Home; Small Family Child Care Home*

## STANDARD 7.007
## DESIGNATION AND ROLE OF STAFF PERSON RESPONSIBLE FOR COORDINATING CARE

If a child has an Individualized Education Program (IEP) or Individualized Family Service Plan (IFSP), the child care facility shall designate one person in the child care setting to be responsible for coordinating care within the facility and with any caregiver or coordinator in other service settings, in accordance with the written plan. Although this person may have other duties, the role of the designated person shall include:
a) Documentation of coordination;
b) Written communication with other care or service providers for the child, to ensure a coordinated, coherent service plan;
c) Sharing information about the plan, staff conferences, written reports, consultations, and other services provided to the child and family. Informed, written parental consent shall be sought before sharing this confidential information;
d) Ensuring implementation of the components of the plan that is relevant to the facility.

When the evaluators are not part of the child care staff, the lead agency shall develop a formal mechanism for coordinating reevaluations and program revisions. The designated staff member from the facility shall routinely be included in the evaluation process and team conferences.

TYPE OF FACILITY: *Center; Large Family Child Care Home; Small Family Child Care Home*

Rationale, comments and references for each Standard are located in *Caring for Our Children, 2nd Edition* (http://nrc.uchsc.edu/CFOC/index.html)

## STANDARD 7.016
# REVIEW OF PLAN FOR SERVING CHILDREN WITH SPECIAL NEEDS

The facility's plan for serving children with special needs shall be reviewed at least annually to see if it is in compliance with the legal requirements of the Americans with Disabilities Act (ADA) and Section 504 of the Rehabilitation Act of 1973 and is achieving the overall objectives for the agency or facility.

TYPE OF FACILITY: *Center; Large Family Child Care Home; Small Family Child Care Home*

# ADDITIONAL STANDARDS FOR PROVIDERS CARING FOR CHILDREN WITH SPECIAL NEEDS

| | |
|---|---|
| Procedures for Obtaining Medical Information | 8.013* |
| Therapy and Treatment Services | 8.016 |
| Health History and Immunizations | 8.046* |
| Parental Participation | 2.050, 2.051, 2.053, 2.057 |
| Parent/Caregiver Collaboration | 2.044* |
| Program Activities | 2.002 |
| Contact with Outside Agencies | 2.058, 2.059 |
| Information Exchange | 8.015, 8.053 |
| Qualifications for Directors | 1.014 |
| Qualifications for Caregiving Staff | 1.017*, 1.019, 1.020 |
| Child:Staff Ratio | 1.001*through 1.003* |
| Health Consultants | 1.040* through 1.044, |
| Orientation Training | 1.023* through 1.025 |
| Continuing Education | 1.029*, 1.030* |
| CPR/First Aid Certification | 1.026* |
| Emergency Plan | 3.049* |
| Transportation | 2.029*, 2.033*, 2.038* |
| Exit Accessibility | 5.021* |
| Facility Accessibility | 5.004* |
| Playroom Floor Space | 5.112* |
| Areas for Therapeutic Intervention | 5.150 |
| Storage for Adaptive Equipment | 5.152 |
| Therapeutic and Recreational Equipment | 5.097 |
| Nutritional Planning | 4.008*, 4.009* |
| Food Allergies | 4.010* |
| Toilet learning/training | 2.005 |
| Seizures (Including Epilepsy) | 3.060*, 3.061* |
| Asthma | 3.062* |
| Special Procedures/Adaptations | 3.063* |
| Special Adaptive Equipment | 1.024*, 5.098, 5.099 |
| Review of Child's Records, Progress, and Future Planning | 8.018 |

*Editor's Note: Standards listed in the chart above with a \* are found in Stepping Stones, 2nd Ed. All others can be found in the Caring for Our Children, 2nd Ed.*

# CHAPTER 8 - ADMINISTRATION

## STANDARD 8.001
## GOVERNING BODY OF THE FACILITY

The facility shall have an identifiable governing body or person with the responsibility for and authority over the operation of the center or program. The governing body shall appoint one person at the facility, or two in the case of co-directors, who is responsible for day-to-day management. The administrator for facilities licensed for more than 100 children shall have no other assigned duties. Responsibilities of the person responsible for the operation of the facility shall include, but shall not be limited to, the following:

a) Ensuring stable and continuing compliance with all applicable rules, regulations, and facility policies and procedures;
b) Developing and implementing policies that promote the achievement of quality child care;
c) Ensuring that all written policies are updated and used, as described in this chapter;
d) Hiring, firing, assigning roles, duties, and responsibility to, supervising, and evaluating personnel;
e) Providing orientation of all new parents, employees, and volunteers to the physical structure, policies, and procedures of the facility. See Orientation Training, STANDARD 1.023 through STANDARD 1.025
f) Notifying all staff, volunteers, and parents of any changes in the facility's policies and procedures;
g) Providing for continuous supervision of visitors and all non-facility personnel;
h) When problems are identified, planning for corrective action, assigning and verifying that a specific person corrects the problem by a specified date;
i) Arranging or providing repair, maintenance, supplemental education, or other services at the facility;
j) Providing or arranging for inservice training for staff and volunteers, based on the needs of the facility and qualifications and skills of staff and volunteers. See Continuing Education, STANDARD 1.029 through STANDARD 1.036;
k) Recommending an annual budget and managing the finances of the facility;
l) Maintaining required records for staff, volunteers, and children at the facility;
m) Providing for parent involvement, including parent education. See Parent Relationships, STANDARD 2.044 through STANDARD 2.057;
n) Reporting to the governing or advisory board on a regular basis as to the status of the facility's operation;

o) Providing oversight of research studies conducted at the facility and joint supervision of students using the facility for clinical practice.

TYPE OF FACILITY: *Center*

## STANDARD 8.008
## CONTENT OF WRITTEN DISCIPLINE POLICY

Each facility shall have and implement a written discipline policy that outlines positive methods of guidance (described in Discipline, STANDARD 2.039 through STANDARD 2.043) appropriate to the ages of the children enrolled. It shall explicitly describe positive, nonviolent, non-abusive methods for achieving discipline. These shall include the following:
a) Redirection;
b) Planning ahead to prevent problems;
c) Encouragement of appropriate behavior;
d) Consistent, clear rules;
e) Children involved in solving problems.

All caregivers shall sign an agreement to implement the facility's discipline policy.

All facilities shall have written discipline policies.

TYPE OF FACILITY: *Center; Large Family Child Care Home, Small Family Child Care Home*

## STANDARD 8.009
## IMPLEMENTATION OF DISCIPLINE POLICY

The caregiver shall implement a policy that promotes positive guidance and discipline techniques and prohibits corporal punishment, psychological abuse, humiliation, abusive language, binding or tying to restrict movement, and the withdrawal or forcing of food and other basic needs, as outlined in STANDARD 2.043. A policy explicitly stating the consequence for staff who exhibit these behaviors shall be determined and reviewed and signed by each staff member prior to hiring.

TYPE OF FACILITY: *Center; Large Family Child Care Home; Small Family Child Care Home*

## STANDARD 8.011
## CONTENT AND DEVELOPMENT OF THE PLAN FOR CARE OF ILL CHILDREN AND CAREGIVERS

The facility's plan for the care of ill children and caregivers shall be developed in consultation with the facility's health consultant. See STANDARD 1.040 through STANDARD 1.044. This plan shall include:

a) Policies and procedures for urgent and emergency care;
b) Admission and inclusion/exclusion policies. Conditions that require that a child be excluded and sent home are specified in Child Inclusion/Exclusion/Dismissal, STANDARD 3.065 through STANDARD 3.068;
c) A description of illnesses common to children in child care, their management, and precautions to address the needs and behavior of the ill child as well as to protect the health of other children and caregivers. See Infectious Diseases, STANDARD 6.001 through STANDARD 6.039;
d) A procedure to obtain and maintain updated individual emergency care plans for children with special health care needs;
e) A procedure for documenting the name of person affected, date and time of illness, a description of symptoms, the response of the caregiver to these symptoms, who was notified (such as a parent, legal guardian, nurse, physician, health department), and the response;
f) The standards described in Reporting Illness, STANDARD 3.087 and STANDARD 3.088; and Notification of Parents, STANDARD 3.084 and STANDARD 3.085.
g) Medication Policy. See STANDARD 8.021.

All child care facilities shall have written policies for the care of ill children and caregivers.

TYPE OF FACILITY: *Center; Large Family Child Care Home; Small Family Child Care Home*

## STANDARD 8.013
## WRITTEN PROCEDURE FOR OBTAINING PREVENTIVE HEALTH SERVICE INFORMATION

Each facility shall develop and follow a written procedure for obtaining necessary medical information including immunizations (see *Recommended Childhood Immunization Schedule* in Appendix G) and periodic preventive health assessments (see *Recommendations for Preventive Pediatric Health Care* in Appendix H) as recommended by the American Academy of Pediatrics (AAP) and the Health Care Financing

Administration of the U.S. Department of Health and Human Services. Facility staff shall encourage parents/legal guardians to schedule these preventive health services in a timely fashion.

Documentation of an age-appropriate health assessment that includes an update of immunizations and screenings shall be filed in the child's record at the facility within 6 weeks of admission and following each subsequent routinely scheduled preventive health care visit. The staff of the facility shall review the admission and all subsequent reports of the child's health assessment visits that occur while the child is enrolled and shall offer a list of concerns for the parents to bring to upcoming check-up visits. Medical information shall include any information needed for the special medical care of the child. Questions raised by child care staff shall be directed to the family or, with parental permission, to the child's health care clinician for explanation and discussion of the implications for care.

Centers shall have written procedures for the verification of compliance with recommended immunizations and periodic health assessments of children. Centers shall maintain confidential records of immunizations, periodic health assessments and any special medical considerations.

TYPE OF FACILITY: *Center; Large Family Child Care Home; Small Family Child Care Home*

## STANDARD 8.022
## WRITTEN PLAN AND TRAINING FOR HANDLING URGENT MEDICAL CARE OR THREATENING INCIDENTS

The facility shall have a written plan for reporting and managing any incident or unusual occurrence that is threatening to the health, safety, or welfare of the children, staff, or volunteers. The facility shall also include procedures of staff training on this plan.

The following incidents, at a minimum, shall be addressed in the plan:
a) Lost or missing child;
b) Suspected sexual, physical, or emotional abuse or neglect of a child (as mandated by state law);
c) Injuries requiring medical or dental care;
d) Serious illness requiring hospitalization, or the death of a child or caregiver, including deaths that occur outside of child care hours.

Rationale, comments and references for each Standard are located in *Caring for Our Children, 2nd Edition* (http://nrc.uchsc.edu/CFOC/index.html)

The following procedures, at a minimum, shall be addressed in the plan:

a) Provision for a caregiver to accompany a child to the source of urgent care and remain with the child until the parent or legal guardian assumes responsibility for the child;

b) Provision for a backup caregiver or substitute (see Substitutes, STANDARD 1.037 through STANDARD 1.039) for large and small family child care homes to make this feasible. Child:staff ratios must be maintained at the facility during the emergency;

c) The source of urgent medical and dental care (such as a hospital emergency room, medical or dental clinic, or other constantly staffed facility known to caregivers and acceptable to parents);

d) Assurance that the first aid kits are resupplied following each first aid incident, and that required contents are maintained in a serviceable condition, by a periodic review of the contents;

e) Policy for scheduled reviews of staff members' ability to perform first aid for averting the need for emergency medical services.

TYPE OF FACILITY: *Center; Large Family Child Care Home; Small Family Child Care Home*

## STANDARD 8.024
## WRITTEN EVACUATION PLAN

The facility shall have a written plan for reporting and evacuating in case of fire, flood, tornado, earthquake, hurricane, blizzard, power failure, bomb threat, or other disaster that could create structural damages to the facility or pose health and safety hazards to the children and staff. The facility shall also include procedures for staff training on this emergency plan.

TYPE OF FACILITY: *Center; Large Family Child Care Home; Small Family Child Care Home*

## STANDARD 8.026
## USE OF DAILY ROSTER DURING DRILLS

The center director or his/her designee shall use a daily class roster in checking the evacuation and return to a safe space for ongoing care of all children and staff members in attendance during an evacuation drill. Small and large family home child caregivers shall count to be sure that all children are safely evacuated and returned to a safe space for ongoing care during an evacuation drill.

TYPE OF FACILITY: *Center; Large Family Child Care Home; Small Family Child Care Home*

# STANDARD 8.027
## APPROVAL AND IMPLEMENTATION OF FIRE EVACUATION PROCEDURE

A fire evacuation procedure shall be approved by a fire inspector for centers and by a local fire department representative for large and small family child care homes during an annual on-site visit when an evacuation drill is observed and the facility is inspected for fire safety hazards. The procedure shall be practiced at least monthly from all exit locations at varied times of the day and during varied activities, including nap time.

TYPE OF FACILITY: *Center; Large Family Child Care Home; Small Family Child Care Home*

# STANDARD 8.028
## AUTHORIZED PERSONS TO PICK UP CHILD

Names, addresses, and telephone numbers of persons authorized to take a child under care out of the facility shall be maintained. The facility shall establish a mechanism for identifying a person for whom the parents have given the facility prior written authorization to pick up their child. Also, policies shall address how the facility will handle the situation if a parent arrives who is intoxicated or otherwise incapable of bringing the child home safely, or if a non-custodial parent attempts to claim the child without the consent of the custodial parent.

TYPE OF FACILITY: *Center; Large Family Child Care Home; Small Family Child Care Home*

# STANDARD 8.029
## POLICY ON ACTIONS TO BE FOLLOWED WHEN NO AUTHORIZED PERSON ARRIVES TO PICK UP A CHILD

Child care facilities shall have a written policy identifying actions to be taken when no authorized person arrives to pick up a child. The plan shall be developed in consultation with the child care health consultant and child protective services.

In the event of emergency situations arising that may make it impossible for a parent to pick up a child as scheduled or to notify the authorized contact to do so, the facility shall attempt to reach each authorized contact, as listed in the facility's records. If these efforts fail, the facility shall immediately implement the written policy on actions to be followed when no authorized person arrives to pick up a child.

TYPE OF FACILITY: *Center; Large Family Child Care Home; Small Family Child Care Home*

## STANDARD 8.036
## INFANT FEEDING POLICIES

Policies about infant feeding shall be developed with the input and approval of the child's health care provider and the Child Care Nutrition Specialist and shall include the following:
a)  Storage and handling of expressed human milk;
b)  Determination of the kind and amount of commercially prepared formula to be prepared for infants as appropriate;
c)  Preparation, storage, and handling of formula;
d)  Proper handwashing of the caregiver;
e)  Use and proper disinfection of feeding chairs and of mechanical food preparation and feeding devices, including blenders, feeding bottles, and food warmers;
f)  Whether formula or baby food shall be provided from home, and if so, how much food preparation and use of feeding devices, including blenders, feeding bottles, and food warmers, shall be the responsibility of the caregiver;
g)  A prohibition against bottle propping or prolonged feeding;
h)  Caregivers shall hold infants during bottle-feeding;
i)  Specification of the number of children who can be fed by one adult at one time;
j)  Handling of food intolerance or allergies (such as to cow's milk, peanuts, orange juice, eggs, or wheat);
k)  Responding to infants' need for food in a flexible fashion to allow demand feedings in a manner that is consistent with the developmental abilities of the child.

Written policies for each infant about infant feeding shall be developed with each individual infant's parents.

TYPE OF FACILITY: *Center; Large Family Child Care Home; Small Family Child Care Home*

## STANDARD 8.038
## POLICIES PROHIBITING SMOKING, TOBACCO, ALCOHOL, ILLEGAL DRUGS, AND TOXIC SUBSTANCES

Facilities shall have written policies specifying that smoking, use of chewing tobacco, use of alcohol, use or possession of illegal drugs, over-use or inappropriate use of prescribed drugs, or unauthorized potentially toxic substances are prohibited in the facility at all times (including outdoor play areas) and during all times when caregivers are responsible for the supervision of children, including times when children are transported and during field trips. The facility shall provide information to employees about available drug, alcohol, and tobacco counseling and rehabilitation and employee assistance programs.

TYPE OF FACILITY: *Center; Large Family Child Care Home; Small Family Child Care Home*

## STANDARD 8.046
## CONTENTS OF CHILD RECORDS

The facility shall maintain a file for each child in one central location within the facility. This file shall be kept in a confidential manner (see Confidentiality and Access to Records, STANDARD 8.053 through STANDARD 8.057) but shall be immediately available to the child's caregivers (who shall have parental consent for access to records), parents or legal guardian, and the licensing authority upon request.

The file for each child shall include the following:
a) Pre-admission enrollment information;
b) Health report and immunization record, completed and signed by the child's health care provider, preferably prior to enrollment or no later than 6 weeks after admission. This record shall document the most recent assessment based on the standard age-related schedule of the American Academy of Pediatrics (AAP);
c) Admission agreement signed by the parent at enrollment;
d) Health history, completed by the parent at admission, preferably with staff involvement;
e) Medication record, maintained on an ongoing basis by designated staff.

TYPE OF FACILITY: *Center; Large Family Child Care Home; Small Family Child Care Home*

Rationale, comments and references for each Standard are located in *Caring for Our Children, 2nd Edition* (http://nrc.uchsc.edu/CFOC/index.html)

# STANDARD 8.048
# CONTENTS OF CHILD'S HEALTH REPORT

The file for each child shall include a health report of an age-appropriate health assessment completed and signed by the child's health care provider. Preferably, this report shall be submitted prior to enrollment, but it shall be submitted no later than 6 weeks after admission. The health report shall include the following medical and developmental information:

a) Records of the child's immunizations;

b) A description of any disability, sensory impairment, developmental variation, seizure disorder, or emotional or behavioral disturbance that may affect adaptation to child care (including previous surgery, serious illness, history of prematurity, if relevant);

c) An assessment of the child's growth based on the percentile for height, weight, and, if the child is younger than 24 months, head circumference;

d) A description of health problems or findings from an examination or screening that needs follow-up;

e) Results of screenings—vision, hearing, dental, nutrition, developmental, tuberculosis, hematocrit or hemoglobin, urine, lead, blood pressure and so forth;

f) Dates of significant communicable diseases (such as chickenpox);

g) Prescribed medication(s), including information on recognizing, documenting, reporting, and responding to potential side effects;

h) A description of current acute or chronic health problems and a special care plan that defines routine and emergency management that might be required by the child while in child care. The care plan for the child with acute or chronic health problems shall include specific instructions for caregiver observations, program activities or services that differ from those required by typically developing children. Such instructions shall include specific teaching and return demonstration of the ability of caregivers to provide medications, procedures, or implement modifications required by children with asthma, severe allergic reactions, diabetes, medically-indicated special feedings, seizures, hearing impairments, vision problems or any other condition that requires accommodation in child care;

i) A description of serious injuries sustained by the child in the past that required medical attention or hospitalization;

j) Other special instructions for the caregiver.

The health report shall include space for additional comments about the management of health problems and for additional health-related data offered by the health care provider or required from the facility.

The health report shall be updated at each age-appropriate health assessment by supplemental notes dated and signed by the child's health

provider on a copy of the previous health report or by submission of a
new report and whenever the child's health status changes.

TYPE OF FACILITY: *Center; Large Family Child Care Home; Small Family Child
Care Home*

## STANDARD 8.051
## CONTENTS OF MEDICATION RECORD

The file for each child shall include a medication record maintained on an
ongoing basis by designated staff. The medication record shall include the
following:
a) Specific signed parent consent for the caregiver to administer
   medication;
b) Prescription by a health care provider, if required;
c) Administration log;
d) Checklist information on medication brought to the facility by the
   parents.

TYPE OF FACILITY: *Center; Large Family Child Care Home; Small Family Child
Care Home*

## STANDARD 8.054
## WRITTEN POLICY ON CONFIDENTIALITY OF
## RECORDS

The facility shall establish and follow a written policy on confidentiality of
the records of staff and children that ensures that the facility will not
disclose material in the records without the written consent of parents
(with legal custody) or legal guardian for children, or of staff for
themselves.

The director of the facility shall decide who among the staff may have
confidential information shared with them. Clearly, this decision must be
made selectively, and all caregivers shall be taught the basic principles of
all individuals' rights to confidentiality.

Written releases shall be obtained from the child's parent or legal
guardian prior to forwarding information and/or the child's records to
other service providers. The content of the written procedures for
protecting the confidentiality of medical and social information shall be
consistent with federal, state, and local guidelines and regulations and
shall be taught to caregivers. Confidential medical information pertinent

Rationale, comments and references for each Standard
are located in *Caring for Our Children, 2nd Edition*
(http://nrc.uchsc.edu/CFOC/index.html)

to safe care of the child shall be provided to facilities within the guidelines of state or local public health regulations. However, under all circumstances, confidentiality about the child's medical condition and the family's status shall be preserved unless such information is released at the written request of the family, except in cases where abuse or neglect is a concern. In such cases, state laws and regulations apply.

TYPE OF FACILITY: *Center*

## STANDARD 8.063
## DOCUMENTATION OF DEATH, INJURY OR ILLNESS

The facility shall document that a child's parent or legal guardian was notified immediately in the event of a death of their child or of an injury or illness of their child that required professional medical attention.

The licensing agency and/or health department shall be notified by the next working day of each of the following events:
a) Injury or illness that required medical attention;
b) Reportable communicable disease;
c) Death;
d) Any other significant event relating to health and safety (such as a lost child, a fire or other structural damage, work stoppage, or closure).

TYPE OF FACILITY: *Center; Large Family Child Care Home; Small Family Child Care Home*

## STANDARD 8.065
## RECORD OF VALID LICENSE, CERTIFICATE OR REGISTRATION OF FACILITY

Every facility shall hold a valid license or certificate of, or documentation of, registration prior to operation as required by the local and/or state statute.

TYPE OF FACILITY: *Center; Large Family Child Care Home; Small Family Child Care Home*

## STANDARD 8.067
## WRITTEN PLAN TO RESOLVE DEFICIENCIES

When deficiencies are identified during annual policy and performance reviews by the licensing department, funding agency, or accreditation organization, the director or small or large family child care home provider shall follow a written plan for resolution, developed with the regulatory agency.

This plan shall include the following:
a)  Description of the problem;
b)  Proposed timeline for resolution;
c)  Designation of responsibility for correcting the deficiency;
d)  Description of the successful resolution of the problem.

For centers, this shall be a written plan.

TYPE OF FACILITY: *Center; Large Family Child Care Home; Small Family Child Care Home*

## STANDARD 8.077
## PUBLIC POSTING OF DOCUMENTS

In a conspicuous place, centers and large family child care homes shall post the following items:
a)  The faculty's license or registration (which also includes the telephone number for filing complaints with the regulatory agency), as specified in Licensing and Legal Records, STANDARD 8.065 through STANDARD 8.067;
b)  A statement informing parents/legal guardians about how they may obtain a copy of the licensing or registration requirements from the regulatory agency;
c)  Information on procedures for filing complaints with the regulatory authority. See Procedures for Complaints and Reporting, RECOMMENDATION 9.020 through RECOMMENDATION 9.022;
d)  Inspection and any accreditation certificates, as specified in Licensing and Legal Records, STANDARD 8.065 and STANDARD 8.066;
e)  Reports of any legal sanctions, as specified in Licensing and Legal Records, STANDARD 8.067;
f)  A notice that inspection reports, legal actions, and compliance letters are available for inspection in the facility;
g)  Evacuation plan, as specified in STANDARD 8.024 through STANDARD 8.027;
h)  Fire evacuation procedures, to be posted in each room of the center;

Rationale, comments and references for each Standard are located in *Caring for Our Children, 2nd Edition* (http://nrc.uchsc.edu/CFOC/index.html)

i) Procedures for the reporting of child abuse consistent with state law and local law enforcement and child protective service contacts;

j) Notice announcing the "open-door policy" (that parents may visit at any time and will be admitted without delay) and the action the facility will take to handle a visitor's request for access if the caregiver is concerned about the safety of the children. See Written Statement of Services, STANDARD 8.045;

k) A roster of the children in each facility room in child care centers, or a list of children in the facility in family child care homes that lists the names of all children who receive care in that room in the center or in the family child care home, the name of the caregiver primarily responsible for each child, and the names of children presently in attendance;

l) A current weekly menu of any food or beverage served in the facility for parents and caregivers. The facility shall provide copies to parents, if requested. Copies of menus served shall be kept on file for 1 year. See also Food Service Records, STANDARD 8.074;

m) A statement of nondiscrimination for programs participating in the United States Department of Agriculture (USDA) Child and Adult Care Food Program;

n) A copy of the policy and procedures for discipline, including the prohibition of corporal punishment. This requirement also applies to school-age child care facilities. See also Discipline Policy, STANDARD 8.008 through STANDARD 8.010;

o) Legible safety rules for the use of swimming and built-in wading pools if the facility has such pools. Safety rules shall be posted conspicuously on the pool enclosure. See also Safety Rules, STANDARD 5.215, and Water Safety, STANDARD 3.045 through STANDARD 3.047;

p) Phone numbers and instructions for contacting the fire department, police, emergency medical services, physicians, dentists, rescue and ambulance services, and the poison control center; the address of the facility; and directions to the facility from major routes north, south, east, and west. This information shall be conspicuously posted adjacent to the telephone;

q) A list of reportable communicable diseases as required by the state and local health authorities. See Reporting Illness, STANDARD 3.086 and STANDARD 3.087;

r) Employee rights and safety standards as required by the Occupational Safety and Health Administration (OSHA) and/or state agencies.

## STANDARD 8.079
## REQUIREMENTS FOR COMPLIANCE OF DROP-IN CARE FACILITIES

Facilities that provide drop-in care (any individual child receives fewer than 30 days of care per year) shall comply with all of the standards except for those in Health Plan for Child Health Services, STANDARD 8.013 through STANDARD 8.017; and Child Records, STANDARD 8.046 through STANDARD 8.052.

Before leaving their child at the child care facility, parents shall provide evidence that the child is up-to-date with recommended immunizations, as specified in Immunizations, STANDARD 3.005 through STANDARD 3.007.

Drop-in care shall not result in licensed capacity being exceeded.

TYPE OF FACILITY: *Center; Large Family Child Care Home*

Rationale, comments and references for each Standard are located in *Caring for Our Children, 2nd Edition* (http://nrc.uchsc.edu/CFOC/index.html)

## Major Occupational Health Hazards

### Infectious Diseases and Organisms

#### General Types of Infectious Diseases

Diarrhea (infectious)

Respiratory tract infection

#### Specific Infectious Diseases and Organisms

Adenovirus

Astrovirus

Caliciviruses

Campylobacter jejuni/coli

Chickenpox (varicella)

Cryptosporidium parvum

Cytomegalovirus (CMV)

Escherichia coli 0157:H7

Giardia lamblia

Hepatitis A

Hepatitis B

Hepatitis C

Herpes 6

Herpes 7

Herpes simplex

Herpes zoster

Human Immunodeficiency Virus (HIV)

Impetigo

Influenza

Lice

Measles

Meningitis (bacterial, viral)

Meningococcus (Neisseria meningitildis)

Mumps

Parvovirus B19

Pertussis

Pinworm

Ringworm

Rotavirus

Rubella

Salmonella organisms

Scabies

Shigella organisms

Staphylococcus aureus

Streptococcus, Group A

Tuberculosis

### Injuries and Noninfectious Diseases

Back injuries

Bites

Dermatitis

Falls

### Environmental exposure

Art materials

Cleaning, sanitizing and disinfecting solutions

Indoor air pollution

Noise

Odor

### Stress

Fear of liability

Inadequate break time, sick time, and personal days

Inadequate facilities

Inadequate pay

Inadequate recognition

Inadequate training

Insufficient professional recognition

Lack of adequate medical/dental health insurance

Responsibility for children's welfare

Undervaluing of work

Working alone

Reference: American Academy of Pediatrics, Committee on Infectious Diseases. *Red Book 2000: Report of the Committee on Infectious Diseases.* Elk Grove Village, Il: American Academy of Pediatrics; 2000.

## Nutrition Specialist and Child Care Food Service Staff Qualifications

| TITLE | LEVEL OF PROFESSIONAL RESPONSIBILITY | EDUCATION AND EXPERIENCE |
| --- | --- | --- |
| **Child Care Nutrition Specialist (state level)** | Develops policies and procedures for implementation of nutrition food standards statewide and provides consultation to state agency personnel, including staff involved with licensure. | Current registration with the Commission on Dietetic Registration of the American Dietetic Association or eligibility for registration with a Bachelor's and Master's degree in nutrition (including or supplemented by course(s) in child growth and development), plus at least 2 years of related experience as a nutritionist in a health program including services to infants and children. A Master's degree from an approved program in public health nutrition may be substituted for registration with the Commission on Dietetic Registration. |
| **Child Care Nutrition Specialist (local level)** | Provides expertise to child care center director and provides ongoing guidance, consultation, and inservice training to facility's nutrition component. The number of sites and facilities for one child care Nutrition Specialist will vary according to size and complexity of local facilities. | Registered Dietitian, as above. At least 1 year of experience as described above. |
| **Child Care Food Service Manager** | Has overall supervisory responsibility for the food service unit at one or more facility sites. | High school diploma or GED. Successful completion of a food handler food protection class. Coursework in basic menu-planning skills, basic foods, introduction to child feeding programs for managers, and/or other relevant courses (offered at community colleges). Two years of food service experience. |
| **Child Care Food Service Worker (Cook)** | Under the supervision of the Food Service Manager, carries out food service operations including menu planning, food preparation and service, and related duties in a designated area. | High school diploma or GED. Successful completion of a food handler food protection class. Coursework in basic menu-planning skills and basic foods (offered through adult education or a community college). One year of food service experience. |
| **Child Care Food Service Aide** | Works no more than 4 hours a day, under the supervision of an employee at a higher level in food service unit. | High school diploma or GED. Must pass the food handler test within 1 to 2 months of employment. No prior experience is required for semi-skilled persons who perform assigned tasks in designated areas. |

# Gloving

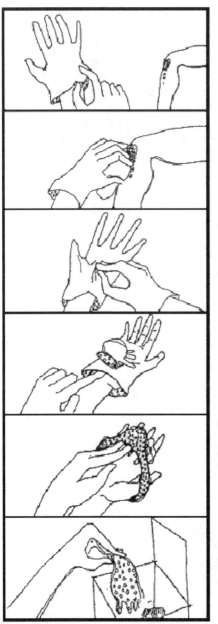

Put on a clean pair of gloves.

Provide the appropriate care.

Remove each glove carefully. Grab the first glove at the palm and strip the glove off. Touch dirty surfaces only to dirty surfaces.

Ball-up the dirty glove in the palm of the other gloved hand.

With the clean hand strip the glove off from underneath at the wrist, turning the glove inside out. Touch dirty surfaces only to dirty surfaces.

Discard the dirty gloves immediately in a step can. Wash your hands.

Reference: California Department of Education. *Keeping Kids Healthy Preventing and Managing Communicable Disease in Child Care.* Sacramento CA:California Department of Education, 1995.

## Recommended Childhood Immunization Schedule

*Editor's note:* Because the American Academy of Pediatrics releases an annual update of the Recommended Childhood Immunization Schedule every January, editors of *Stepping Stones, 2nd Edition* made the decision to not include the actual schedule in this document as *Stepping Stones'* longevity will surpass the current year. Please refer to the American Academy of Pediatrics' web site - http://www.aap.org for the most recent edition or obtain a copy of the current January issue of *Pediatrics* in which the schedule is published. Web access and copies of the journal can be found at or obtained through a local public library. Also local health departments can often supply a copy of the most recent schedule. Contact information for the American Academy of Pediatrics is located in Appendix BB.

## Recommendations for Preventive Pediatric Health Care

*Editor's note:* Because the American Academy of Pediatrics releases a periodic update of the Recommendations for Preventive Pediatric Health Care, editors of *Stepping Stones, 2nd Edition* made the decision to not include the actual schedule in this document as *Stepping Stones'* longevity will surpass the current edition. Please refer to the American Academy of Pediatrics' web site - http://www.aap.org for the most recent edition.  Local health departments can often supply a copy of the most recent schedule. Contact information for the American Academy of Pediatrics is located in Appendix BB.

# Special Care Plan for a Child with Asthma

**Child's Name:**_____  **Date of Birth:**_____
**Parent(s) or Guardian(s) Name:**_____
**Emergency phone numbers**: Mother_____ Father_____
  *(see emergency contact information for alternate contacts if parents are unavailable)*
**Primary health provider's name:** _____ **Emergency Phone:**_____
**Asthma specialist's name** (if any): _____ **Emergency Phone:**_____

**Known triggers** for this child's asthma (circle all that apply):

| | | | |
|---|---|---|---|
| colds | mold | exercise | tree pollens |
| house | dust | strong odors | grass flowers |
| excitement | weather changes | animals | smoke |
| foods (specify): _____ | | | room deodorizers |
| other (specify): _____ | | | |

**Activities** for which this child has needed special attention in the past (circle all that apply)

| *outdoors* | *indoors* |
|---|---|
| field trip to see animals | kerosene/wood stove heated rooms |
| running hard | art projects with chalk, glues, fumes |
| gardening | sitting on carpets |
| jumping in leaves | pet care |
| outdoors on cold or windy days | recent pesticides application in facility |
| playing in freshly cut grass | painting or renovation in facility |
| other (specify):_____ | |

Can this child use a **flowmeter** to monitor need for medication in child care?   NO   YES
personal best reading: _____reading to give extra dose of medicine:_____
                                    reading to get medical help:_____
How often has this child needed urgent care from a doctor for an attack of asthma:
in the past 12 months?_____in the past 3 months?_____

**Typical signs and symptoms** of the child's asthma episodes (circle all that apply):

| | | |
|---|---|---|
| fatigue | face red, pale or swollen | grunting |
| breathing faster | wheezing | sucking in chest/neck |
| restlessness,agitation | dark circles under eyes | persistent coughing |
| complaints of chest pain/tightness | | gray or blue lips or fingernails |
| flaring nostrils, mouth open (panting) | | difficulty playing, eating, drinking, talking |

*Reminders:*
1. *Notify parents immediately if emergency medication is required.*
2. *Get emergency medical help if.*
- *the child does not improve 15 minutes after treatment and family cannot be reached*
- *after receiving a treatment for wheezing, the child:*
- • *is working hard to breathe or grunting*   • *won't play*
- • *is breathing fast at rest (>50/min)*   • *has gray or blue lips or fingernails*
- • *has trouble walking or talking*   • *cries more softly and briefly*
- • *has nostrils open wider than usual*   • *is hunched over to breathe*
- •*has sucking in of skin (chest or neck) with breathing*• *is extremely agitated or sleepy*
3. *Child's doctor & child care facility should keep a current copy of this form in child's record.*

Reprinted with permission from Child Care and Children with Special Needs Workbook.
Wilmington, DE: Video Active Productions, 2001; 302-477-9440

## Special Care Plan for a Child with Asthma (Continued)

| **Medications** for routine and emergency treatment of asthma for: | | | |
|---|---|---|---|
| Child's name | | Date of Birth | |
| **Name of medication** | | | |
| **When to use (e.g., symptoms, time of day, frequency, etc.)** | *routine or emergency* | *routine or emergency* | *routine or emergency* |
| **How to use (e.g.,by mouth, by inhaler, with or without spacing device, in nebulizer, with or without dilution, diluting fluid, etc.)** | | | |
| **Amount (dose) of medication** | | | |
| **How soon treatment should start to work** | | | |
| **Expected benefit for the child** | | | |
| **Possible side effects, if any** | | | |
| **Date instructions were last updated by child's doctor** | Date: _____ Name of Doctor (print): _____ <br> Doctor's signature:_____ | | |
| **Parent's permission to follow this medication plan** | Date:_____ Parent's signature: _____ | | |

*If more columns are needed for medication or equipment instruction, copy this page*

Reprinted with permission from Child Care and Children with Special Needs Workbook. Wilmington, DE: Video Active Productions, 2001; 302-477-9440

**The Academy of Breastfeeding Medicine**
P.O. Box 15945-284
Lenexa, KS 66285-5945
Phone: 913-541-9077
Fax: 913-541-0156
http://bfmed.org

**American Academy of Allergy, Asthma, and Immunology(AAAAI)**
611 East Wells Street
Milwaukee, WI 53202
Phone: 414-272-6071
Fax: 414-272-6070
http://www.aaaai.org
Email:info@aaaai.org

**American Academy of Family Physicians (AAFP)**
11400 Tomahawk Creek Pkwy.
Leawood, KS. 66211
Phone: 800-274-2237 or 913-906-6000
http://www.aafp.org

**American Academy of Pediatrics (AAP)**
141 Northwest Point Boulevard
Elk Grove Village, IL 60007-1098
Phone: 847-434-4000
Fax: 847-228-5097
http://www.aap.org

**American Academy of Pediatric Dentistry**
211 East Chicago Avenue, #700
Chicago, IL 60611-2663
Phone: 312-337-2169
Fax: 312-337-6329
http://www.aapd.org
E-mail: info@aapd.org

**American Alliance for Health, Physical Education, Recreation, & Dance**
1900 Association Drive
Reston, VA 20191-1502
Phone: 1-800-213-7193
Fax: 703-476-9527
E-mail: webmaster@aahperd.org
http://www.aahperd.org

**American Association of Family and Consumer Services**
1555 King St.
Alexandria, VA 22314
Phone: 703-706-4600
Fax: 703-706-4663
http://www.staff.aafcs.org

**American Association for Health Education (AAHE)**
1900 Association Drive
Reston, VA 20191-1599
Phone: 1-800-213-7193 or 703-476-3437
Fax: 703-476-6638
E-mail: aahe@ahhperd.org
http://www.aahperd.org/aahe

**American Automobile Association (AAA)**
1000 AAA Dr.
Heathrow, FL 32746
Phone: 407-444-4240
Fax: 407-444-4247
http://www.aaa.com

**American Cancer Society**
1599 Clifton Road NE
Atlanta, GA 30329-4251
Phone: 1-800-227-2345 or 404-320-3333
http://www.cancer.org

**American College of Emergency Physicians**
1125 Executive Circle
Irving, TX 75038-2522,
Phone: 1-800-798-1822
http://www.acep.org

**American Diabetes Association**
1701 North Beauregard Street
Alexandria, VA 22311
Phone: 800-342-2383
Fax: 703-549-6995
E-mail: customerservice@diabetes.org
http://www.diabetes.org

**American Dietetic Association (ADA)**
216 West Jackson Boulevard
Chicago, Illinois 60606-6995
Phone: 312-899-0040
Fax: 312-899-1979
http://www.eatright.org

**Americans with Disabilities Act Accessibility Guidelines (ADAAG)**
U.S. Department of Justice
Civil Rights Division
Disability Rights Section
P.O. Box 66738
Washington, DC 20035-6738
Phone: 1-800-514-0301
Phone (TDD): 1-800-514-0383
http://www.usdoj.gov/crt/ada/adahom1.htm

**American Furniture Manufacturer's Association (AFMA)**
P.O. Box HP-7
High Point, NC 27261
Phone: 336-884-5000
Fax: 336-884-5303
http://www.afma4u.org

**The American Gas Association**
1515 Wilson Blvd.
Arlington, VA 22209
Phone: 703-841-8400
http://www.aga.org

**American Heart Association (AHA)**
7272 Greenville Avenue
Dallas, Texas 75231
Phone: 214-373-6300
http://www.amhrt.org

**American Lifeguard Association**
8150 Leesburg Pike #600
Vienna, VA. 22182
Phone: 703-748-4803
Fax: 1-888-432-9252

**American Lung Association**
432 Park Ave. South
New York, NY 10016
Phone: 212-889-3370
Fax: 212-889-3375
http://www.alany.org

**American National Standards Institute (ANSI)**
1819 L Street, NW, 6th Fl.
Washington, DC, 20036
Phone: 202-293-8020
Fax: 202-293-9287
E-mail: ansionline@ansi.org
http://www.ansi.org

**American Nurses Association (ANA)**
600 Maryland Ave., SW
Suite 100 West
Washington, DC 20024
Phone: 1-800-274-4262 or 202-651-7000
Fax: 202-651-7001
http://www.nursingworld.org

**American Public Health Association (APHA)**
800 I Street N.W,
Washington, DC 20001-3710
Phone: 202-777-APHA(2742)
Fax: 202-777-2534
http://www.apha.org
E-mail: comments@apha.org

**American Red Cross (ARC)**
4333 Arlington Blvd.
Arlington, VA 22203-2904
Phone: 703-527-3010
Fax: 703-527-2705
http://www.redcross.org

**American School Food Service Association**
700 South Washington St.
Suite 300
Alexandria, VA 22314-4287
Phone: 703-739-3900
Fax: 703-739-3915
E-mail: servicecenter@asfsa.org
http://www.asfsa.org

**American Society of Heating, Refrigerating, and Air Conditioning Engineers (ASHRAE)**
1791 Tullie Circle, NE
Atlanta, GA 30329
Phone: 404-636-8400
Fax: 404-321-5478
http://www.ashrae.org

**American Society for Testing and Materials (ASTM)**
100 Barr Harbor Drive
West Conshohocken, PA 19428-2959
Phone: 610-832-9500
Fax: 610-832-9555
http://www.astm.org

**Art and Creative Materials Institute (ACMI)**
1280 Main St.
PO Box 479
Hanson, MA 02341
Phone: 781-293-4100
Fax: 781-294-0808
http://www.acminet.org

**Association of Home Appliance Manufacturers**
1111 19th St. N.W.
Washington, DC 20036
Phone: 202-872-5955
Fax: 202-872-9354
http://www.aham.org

**Asthma and Allergy Foundation of America**
1233 20th St., N.W.
Suite 402
Washington, DC 20036
Phone: 1-800-727-8462
Fax: 202-466-8940
http://www.aafa.org

**Boy Scouts**
1325 West Walnut Hill Lane
PO Box 152079
Irving, TX 75015-2079
Phone: 972-580-2000
Fax: 972-580-2502
http://www.bsa.scouting.org

**Building Officials & Code Administrators International**
4051 W. Flossmoor Rd.
Country Club Hills, IL 60478
Phone: 708-799-2300
Fax: 708-799-4981
E-mail: info@bocai.org
http://www.bocai.org

**Canadian Paediatric Society**
100-2204 Walkley Rd.
Ottawa ON K1G 4G8
Phone: 613-526-9397
Fax: 613-526-3332
http://www.cps.ca
E-mail: info.cps.ca

**Canadian Standards Association (CSA)**
178 Rexdale Boulevard
Toronto, ON
M9W 1R3, CANADA
Phone: 1-800-463-6727
Fax: 416-747-2510
E-mail: info@csa-international.org
http://www.csa.ca

**Center for the Child Care Workforce (CCW)**
733 15th Street, NW Suite 1037
Washington, DC 20005-2112
Phone: 1-800-879-6784
Fax: 202-737-0370
E-mail: ccw@ccw.org
http://www.ccw.org

**Centers for Disease Control and Prevention (CDC)**
1600 Clifton Road NE
Atlanta, GA 30333
1-800-311-3534
http://www.cdc.gov

**Child Care Action Campaign (CCAC)**
330 Seventh Avenue, 14th Floor
New York, NY 10001
Phone: 212-239-0138 or 1-800-424-2246
Fax: 212-268-6515
http://www.childcareation.org

**Child Care Bureau**
Administration for Children and Families
U.S. Department of Health and Human Services
Switzer Building, Room 2046
330 C Street SW
Washington, DC 20447
Phone: 202-690-6782
Fax: 202-690-5600
E-mail: ccb@acf.dhhs.gov
http://www.acf.dhhs.gov/programs/ccb

**Child Care Law Center**
973 Market Street, Suite 550
San Francisco, CA 94103
Phone: 415-495-5498
Fax: 415-495-6734
http://www.childcarelaw.org

**Child Care Nutrition Resource System**
Food and Nutrition Information Center
National Agricultural Library10301 Baltimore Avenue
Beltsville, MD 20705-2351
Phone: 301-504-5719
http://www.nal.usda.gov/childcare

**Children's Safety Network**
CSN National Injury and Violence Prevention
Resource Center
Education Development Center, Inc.
55 Chapel Street
Newton, MA 02458-1060
Phone: 617-969-7100
Fax: 617-969-9186
http://www.edc.org/HHD/csn

**Consumer Product Safety Commission,
US (CPSC)**
1-800-638-2772
http://www.cpsc.gov

**Cooperative State Research, Education,
and Extension Service**
U.S. Department of Agriculture
Washington, D.C. 20250-0900
Phone: 202-720-4651
Fax: 202-690-0289
E-mail: csrees@reeusda.gov
http://www.reeusda.gov

**Dairy Council**
10255 West Higgins Road
Suite 900
Rosemont, IL 60018-5616
Phone: 847-803-2000
http://www.nationaldairycouncil.org

**Disability and Business Technical Assis-
tance
Centers**
(American with Disabilities Act Experts)
1-800-949-4232

**Early Childhood Education Linkage Sys-
tem (ECELS)**
Healthy Child Care America Pennsylvania
Pennsylvania Chapter, American Academy of
Pediatrics
Rosemont Business Campus
Building 2, Suite 307
919 Conestoga Road
Rosemont, PA 19010
Phone: 610-520-3662
http://www.paaap.org

**The Edison Electric Institute**
701 Pennsylvania Ave., NW
Washington, DC 20004-2696
Phone: 202-508-5000
http://www.eei.org

**Emergency Medical Services for Children
National Resource Center**
111 Michigan Avenue, N.W.
Washington, DC 20010-2970
Phone: 202-884-4927
Fax: 202-884-6845
http://www.ems-c.org

**Environmental Protection Agency (EPA)**
401 M Street SW
Washington, DC 20460-0003
Phone: 202-260-2090
http://www.epa.gov

**Federal Bureau of Investigation (FBI)**
J. Edgar Hoover Building
935 Pennsylvania Avenue, N.W
Washington, D.C. 20535-0001
Phone: 202-324-3000
http://www.fbi.gov

**Food & Nutrition Information Center**
Agricultural Research Service, USDA
National Agricultural Library, Room 105
10301 Baltimore Avenue
Beltsville, MD 20705-2351
Phone: 301-504-5719
Fax: 301-504-6409
http://www.nal.usda.gov/fnic
E-mail: fnic@nal.usda.gov

**Food Research Action Center**
1875 Connecticut Avenue, N.W., Suite 540
Washington, D.C. 20009
Phone: 202-986-2200
Fax: 202-986-2525
E-mail: webmaster@frac.org
http://www.frac.org

**The Healthy Child Care America Cam-
paign**
American Academy of Pediatrics
141 N.W. Point Blvd.
Elk Grove Village, IL 60007
Phone: 888-227-5409
Fax: 847-228-6432
E-mail: childcare@aap.org

**Institute of Electrical & Electronics Engineers (IEEE)**
445 Hoes Lane
Piscataway, NJ 08855-1331
Phone: 732-981-0060
Fax: 303-758-1138
E-mail: askieee@ieee.org
http://www.ieee.org

**Juvenile Products Manufacturers Association (JPMA)**
17000 Commerce Pkwy. Suite C
Mt. Laurel, NJ 08054
http://www.jpma.org

**La Leche League International**
1400 N. Meacham Rd.
Schaumburg, IL 60173-4048
Phone: 847-519-7730
Fax: 847-519-0035
http://www.lalecheleague.org

**Maternal and Child Health Bureau (MCHB)**

**MCHB Region I**
Room 1826
John F. Kennedy Federal Building
Boston MA 02203
Phone: 617-565-1433
Fax: 617-565-3044
States - CT, ME, MA, NH, RI, VT

**MCHB Region II**
26 Federal Plaza
Federal Building, Room 3835
New York, N.Y. 10278
Phone: 212-264-2571
Fax: 212-264-2673
States - NJ, NY, PR, VI

**MCHB Region III**
Health Resources, Northeast Cluster
Public Ledger Building
150 S. Independence Mall West
Suite 1172
Philadelphia, PA 19106-3499
Phone: 215-861-4422
Fax: 215-861-4385
States - DE, DC, MD, PA, VA, WV

**MCHB Region IV**
HRSA Field Coordinator, Southeast Cluster
Atlanta Federal Center
61 Forsyth Street, S.W., Suite 3M60
Atlanta, GA 30303-8909
Phone: 404-562-7980
Fax: 404-562-7974
States - AL, FL, GA, KY, MS, NC, SC, TN

**MCHB Region V**
105 W. Adams Street, 17th Floor
Chicago, IL 60603
Phone: 312-353-4042
Fax: 312-886-3770
States - IL, IN, MI, MN, OH, WI

**MCHB Region VI**
1301 Young Street, 10th Floor, HRSA-4
Dallas, TX 75202
Phone: 214-767-3003
Fax: 214-767-3038
States - AR, LA, NM, OK, TX

**MCHB Region VII**
Federal Building, Room 501
601 E. 12th Street
Kansas City, MO 64106-2808
Phone: 816-426-5292
Fax: 816-426-3633
States - IA, KS, MO, NE

**MCHB Region VIII**
Federal Office Building, Room 409
1961 Stout Street
Denver, CO 80294
Phone: 303-844-7862
Fax: 303-844-0002
States - CO, MT, ND, SD, UT, WY

**MCHB Region IX**
Federal Office Building, Room 317
50 United Nations Plaza
San Francisco, CA 94102
Phone: 415-437-8101
Fax: 415-437-8105
States - AZ, CA, HI, NV, AS, FM, GU, MH, MP, PW

**MCHB Region X**
Mail Stop RX-23
2201 Sixth Avenue, Room 700,
Seattle, WA 98121
Phone: 206-615-2518
Fax: 206-615-2500
http://www.mchb.hrsa.gov
States - AK, ID, OR, WA

**National Association for the Education of Young Children (NAEYC)**
1509 16th Street, NW
Washington DC 20036
Phone: 1-800-424-2460
http://www.naeyc.org

**National Association for Family Child Care (NAFCC)**
5202 Pinemont Drive
Salt Lake City, UT 84123
Phone: 801-269-9338
http://www.nafcc.org

**National Association of Child Care Resource and Referral Agencies**
1319 F Street, NW Suite 500
Washington, DC 20004-1106
Phone: 202-393-5501
Fax: 202-393-1109
E-mail: info@naccrra.org
http://www.naccrra.org

**National Association of Diaper Services**
994 Old Eagle School Road, #1019
Wayne, PA 19087
Phone: 610-971-4850
http://www.diapernet.com

**National Association of Governor's Councils of Physical Fitness and Sports**
401 W. Michigan St.
Indianapolis, IN 46202
Phone: 317-237-5630
Fax: 317-237-5632
E-mail: info@physicalfitness.org
http://www.physicalfitness.org

**National Association of Pediatric Practitioners (NAPNAP)**
20 Brace Road, Suite 200
Cherry Hill, NJ 08034
Phone: 856-857-9700
Fax: 856-857-1600
http://www.napnap.org

**National Association for Regulatory Administration**
26 East Exchange Street, Fifth Floor
St. Paul, MN 55101-2264
Phone: 651-290-6280
Fax: 651-290-2266
http://www.nara-licensing.org

**National Association for Sick Child Day-care (NASCD)**
1716 5th. Ave. N.
Birmingham, AL 35203
Phone: 202-324-8447
Fax: 202-324-8050
E-mail: gwj@nascd.com
http://www.nascd.com

**National Association of WIC Directors**
2001 S Street, NW
Suite 580
Washington, DC 20009
Phone: 202-232-5492
Fax: 202-387-5281
http://www.wicdirectors.org

**National Center for Cultural Competence**
Georgetown University Child Development Center
3307 M Street, NW, Suite 401
Washington, DC 20007-3935
Phone: 800-788-2066
Fax: 202-687-8899
http://gucdc.georgetown.edu/nccc
E-mail: cultural@georgetown.edu

**National Center for Education in Maternal and Child Health (NCEMCH)**
2000 15th Street, North, Suite 701
Arlington, VA 22201-2617
Phone: 703-524-7802
Fax: 703-524-9335
E-mail: info@ncemch.org
http://www.ncemch.org

**National Child Care Information Center**
(Funded by the Child Care Bureau)
243 Church Street, NW 2nd Floor
Vienna, VA 22180
Phone: 1-800-616-2242
Fax: 1-800-716-2242
TTY: 1-800-516-2242
http://www.nccic.org

**National Clearinghouse on Child Abuse and Neglect Information**
330 C Street, SW
Washington, DC 20447
Phone: 800-394-3366
Fax: 703-385-3206
http://www.calib.com/nccanch

**National Child Care Association (NCCA)**
1016 Rosser Street
Conyers, GA 30012
Phone: 1-800-543-7161
Fax: 770-388-7772
http://www.nccanet.org

**National Commission for Health Education Credentialing, Inc. (NCHEC)**
944 Marcon BLVD., Suite 310
Allentown, PA 18103
Phone: 1-888-624-3248
Fax: 1-800-813-0727
E-mail: nchectce@fast.net
http://www.nchec.org

**National Committee for the Prevention of Child Abuse**
PO Box 2866
Chicago, IL 60690-9950
Phone: 312-663-3520
http://www.childabuse.org
E-mail: mail@preventchildabuse.org

**National Fire Protection Association (NFPA)**
1 Battery March Park
Quince, MA 02269-9101
Phone: 617-770-3000
Fax: 617-770-0700
http://www.nfpa.org

**National Food Service Management Institute**
The University of Mississippi
P.O. Drawer 188
University, MS 38677-0188
Phone: 1-800-321-3054
Fax: 1-800-321-3061
http://www.nfsmi.org

**National Heart, Lung, and Blood Institute**
Health Information Center
P.O. Box 30105
Bethesda, MD
Phone: 301-592-8573
Fax: 301-592-8563
E-mail: NHLBInfo@rover.nhlbi.nih.gov
http://www.nhlbi.nih.gov/health/infoctr/index.htm

**National Healthy Mothers, Healthy Babies Coalition**
121 North Washington St.
Suite 300
Alexandria, VA 22314
Phone: 703-836-6110
Fax: 703-836-3470
http://www.hmhb.org

**National Highway and Transportation Safety Administration (NHTSA)**

**NHTSA Region I**
Kendall Square Code 903
Cambridge, MA 02142
Phone: 617-494-3427
Fax: 617-494-3646
States - CT, ME, MA, NH, RI, VT

**NHTSA Region II**
222 Mamaroneck Avenue Suite 204
White Plains, NY 10605
Phone: 914-682-6162
Fax: 914-682-6239 Fax
States - NY, NJ, PR, VI

**NHTSA Region III**
10 South Howard Street
Suite 6700
Baltimore, MD 21201
Phone: 410-962-0090
Fax: 410-962-2770
States - DE, DC, MD, PA, VA, WV

**NHTSA Region IV**
61 Forsyth Street, SW
Suite 17T30
Atlanta, GA 30303
Phone: 404-562-3739
Fax: 404-562-3763
States - AL, FL, GA, KY, MS, NC, SC, TN

**NHTSA Region V**
19900 Governors Drive, Suite 201
Olympia Fields, IL 60461
Phone: 708-503-8822
Fax: 708-503-8991 Fax
States - IL, IN, MI, MN, OH, WI

**NHTSA Region VI**
819 Taylor Street Room 8a38
Fort Worth, TX 76102-6177
Phone: 817-978-3653
Fax: 817-978-8339 Fax
States - AR, LA, NM, OK, TX, Indian N.

**NHTSA Region VII**
901 Locust Street Rm466
Kansas City, MO 64106
Phone: 816-329-3900
Fax: 816-329-3910
States - IA, KS, MO, NE

**NHTSA Region VIII**
555 Zang Street, Room 430
Lakewood, Colorado 80228
Phone: 303-969-6917
Fax: 303-969-6294 fax
States - CO, MT, ND, SD, UT, WY

**NHTSA Region IX**
201 Mission Street, Suite 2230
San Francisco, CA 94105
Phone: 415-744-3089
Fax: 415-744-2532 Fax
States - AZ, CA, HI, NV, Amer. Samoa, Guam,
Mariana Island

**NHTSA Region X**
3140 Jackson Federal Building
915 Second Avenue
Seattle, WA 98174
Phone: 206-220-7640
Fax: 206-220-7651
Phone: 1-888-327-4236
http://www.nhtsa.dot.gov
States - AK, ID, OR, WA

**National Information Center for Children
and Youth with Disabilities**
P.O. Box 1492
Washington, DC 20013-1492
Phone: 1-800-695-0285
E-mail: nichcy@aed.org
http://www.nichcy.org

**National Institute of Health, National
Institute of Child Health and Human
Development**
P.O.box 3006
Rockville, MD 20847
Phone: 1-800-370-2943
Fax: 301-984-1473
E-mail: nichdclearinghouse@mail.nih.gov
http://www.nichd.nih.gov

**National Maternal and Child Health
Clearinghouse**
2070 Chain Bridge Road, Suite 450
Vienna, VA 22182-2536
Phone: 1-888-434-4624
Fax: 703-821-2098
E-Mail: nmchc@circlesolutions.com
http://www.nmchc.org

**National OnSite Wastewater Recycling
Association, Inc. (NOWRA)**
632 Main Street
Laurel, MD 20707
Phone: 301-776-7468
Fax: 301-776-7409
http:// www.nowra.org

**National Recreation and Park Association**
22377 Belmont Ridge Road
Ashburn, VA 20148
Phone: (703) 858-0784
Fax: (703) 858-0794
http://www.nrpa.org

**National Resource Center for Health and
Safety in Child Care**
University of Colorado School of Nursing
Campus Mail Stop F541, P.O. Box 6508
Aurora, CO 80045-0508
Phone: 1-800-598-5437
Fax: 303-724-0960
http://nrc.uchsc.edu

**National Safety Council (NSC)**
1121 Spring Lake Drive,
Itasca, IL 60143-3201
Phone: 630-285-1121
Fax: 630-285-0797
http://www.nsc.org

**National Sanitation Foundation (NSF)**
PO Box 130140
Ann Arbor, MI 48113-0140
Phone: 800-673-6275 or 734-769-8010
Fax: 734-769-0109
http://www.nsf.org

**National School-Age Care Alliance**
1137 Washington Street
Boston, MA 02124
Phone: 617-298-5012
Fax: 617-298-5022
http://www.nsaca.org

**National SIDS Resource Center**
2070 Chain Bridge Road, Suite 450
Vienna, VA 22182
Phone: 703-821-8955
Fax: 703-821-2098
E-mail: sids@circlesolutions.com
http://www.sidscenter.org

**National Technical Information Service (NTIS)**
5285 Port Royal Road
Springfield, Virginia 22161
Phone: 703-605-6000
Fax: 703-605-6900
E-mail: info@ntis.gov
http://www.ntis.gov

**National Training Institute for Child Care Health Consultants**
Department of Maternal and Child Health
University of North Carolina at Chapel Hill
116A S. Merritt Mill Rd. Box 8126
Chapel Hill, NC 27599-8126
Phone: 919-966-3780
Fax: 919-843-4752
E-mail: nticchc@sph.unc.edu

**National Weather Service**
1352 East-West Highway
Silver Spring, MD 20910
http://www.nws.noaa.gov

**Occupational Health & Safety Administration (OSHA)**
200 Constitution Avenue, N.W.
Washington, D.C. 20210
Phone: 202-693-1999
http://www.osha.gov
(Web site of OSHA Regional Office Contacts)

**Office of Special Education & Rehabilitative Services**
U.S. Department of Education
330 C Street S.W.
Washington, DC 20202
Phone: 202-205-5465
Fax: 202-205-9252
http://www.ed.gov/offices/OSERS

**Oregon Child Development Coalition**
PO Box 2780
9140 SW Pioneer Court, Suite E
Wilsonville, OR 97070
Phone: 503-570-1110
Fax: 503-682-9426
http://ocdc.net

**Presidents Challenge Physical Fitness Program**
400 E. 7th Street
Bloomington, IN 47405
Phone: 1-800-258-8146
Fax: 812-855-8999
E-mail: preschal@indiana.edu
http://www.indiana.edu/~preschal

**President's Council on Physical Fitness & Sports**
200 Independence Avenue SW.
Humphrey Building, Room 738 H
Washington, DC 20201
Phone: 202-690-9000
Fax: 202-690-5211
http://www.fitness.gov

**Project Child**
2200 West Broad Street
Bethlehem, PA 18018-3200
Phone: 610-419-4500
Fax: 610-419-3888
E-mail: project childlv@aol.com

**Seattle King County Department of Public Health**
999 3rd Ave. Suite 1200
Seattle, WA 98104
Phone: (206) 296-4600
http://www.metrokc.gov/health

**Shape Up America**
4500 Connecticut Ave. N.W.
Washington, DC 20008
Phone: 301-493-5368
Fax: 301-493-9504
E-mail: suainfo@shapeup.org
http://www.shapeup.org

**Snell Memorial Foundation**
3628 Madison Avenue, Suite 11
North Highlands, CA 95660
Phone: 916-331-5073
Fax: 916-331-0359
http://www.smf.org/snell.html

**Society for Nutrition Education**
1001 Connecticut Avenue, NW Suite 528
Washington, DC 20036-5528
Phone: 202-452-8534
Fax: 202-452-8536
E-mail: membership@sne.org
http://www.sne.org

**State and Territorial Injury Prevention
Directors' Association**
2141Kingston Court, Suite 110-B
Marietta, GA 30067
Phone:770-690-9000
Fax: 770-690-8996
E-mail:
http://www.stipda.org/

**Superintendent of Documents**
U.S. Government Printing Office
Washington, DC 20402
Phone: 202-512-2000
http://www.gpo.gov

**Tribal Child Care Technical Assistance
Center (TriTAC)**
(Funded by the Child Care Bureau)
Phone: 1-800-388-7670
http://nccic.org/tribal

**Underwriters Laboratories (UL)**
333 Pfingsten Road
Northbrook, IL 60062-2096
Phone: 847-272-8800
Fax: 847-272-8129
E-mail: northbrook@us.ul.com
http://www.ul.com

**US Department of Energy**
1000 Independence Ave.
Washington, DC 20585
Phone: 202-586-5000
http://www.energy.gov

**US Consumer Product Safety Commission See Consumer Product Safety Commission, US**

**US Food and Drug Administration (FDA)**
HFI-40
Rockville, MD 20857
Phone: 1-888-463-6332
http://www.fda.gov

**USDA Food and Nutrition Service**
3101 Park Center Drive
Alexandria, VA 22302
Phone: 703-305-2062
http://www.fns.usda.gov

**USDA Food Safety and Inspection Service**
Room 1175-South Building
1400 Independence Ave. SW
Washington, DC 20250
Phone: (202) 720-7943
http://www.fsis.usda.gov

**Visiting Nurse Associations of America**
11 Beacon Street, Suite 910
Boston, MA 02108
617-523-4042
http://www.vnaa.org

**Wheelock College Institute for Leadership
and Career Initiatives**
200 The Riverway
Boston, MA 02215
Phone: 617-734-5200 x2211
Fax: 617-738-0643
http://institute.wheelock.edu

**YMCA**
101 North Wacker Dr.
Chicago, IL 60606
Phone: 312-977-0031
Fax: 312-977-9063
http://www.ymca.net

# CONTRIBUTORS TO REVISION PROCESS

## Technical Panel Chairs and Members Who Participated in Review

### Children With Special Needs
**Herbert J. Cohen, MD, FAAP, Chair,** Bronx, NY
Rebecca Fewell, PhD, Nashville, TN
Ruth Kaminer, MD, FAAP, Bronx, NY
Lillian Kornhaber, RPT, Bronx, NY
Anne Riley, RN, Iowa City, IA
Sarah Schoen, MA, OT, Bronx, NY

### Environmental Quality
**Steven B. Eng, MPH, RPHI, Chair,** BC, Canada
Alison Freeman, Washington, DC
Shannan Lile, RS, Arlington, TX
Lori Saltzman, Bethesda, MD
Richard K. Snaman, REHS/RS, Arlington, VA

### General Health
**Selma Deitch, MD, MPH, FAAP, Chair,** Manchester, NH
Linda Kincaid, BSN, RN, Manchester, NH
Steven Grandgeorge, MD, FAAP, Bedford, NH
Richard Nordgren, MD, Lebanon, NH
Mary Jane Wallner, Concord, NH

### Health and Safety Organization and Administration
**Christopher Kus, MD, MPH, Chair,** Albany, NY
Michelle Cravetz, MS, Albany, NY
Kim Keiser, Waterbury, VT
Karen E. Kroh, BA, Harrisburg, PA
Shirley Norris, MA, Topeka, KS
Peggy Scally, RN, Lawrence, KS

### Health Concerns Related to Social Environment and Child Development
**Angela Crowley, PhD, APRN, CS, PNP, Chair,** New Haven, CT
Joseph Avni-Singer, MD, New Haven, CT
Carla Horwitz, EdD, MS, New Haven, CT
Michael Kaplan, MD, New Haven, CT
Kathryn Taeffe McLearn, PhD, New York, NY
June Sale, Los Angeles, CA

## Infectious Diseases
**Larry Pickering, MD, FAAP, Chair,** Atlanta, GA
Ralph L. Cordell, PhD, Atlanta, GA
Fred Henderson, MD, Chapel Hill, NC
Dennis L. Murray, MD, FAAP, Augusta, GA
Robert F. Pass, MD, FAAP, Birmingham, AL

## Injury Prevention
**Albert Chang, MD, MPH, FAAP, Chair,** San Diego, CA
Abbey Alkon, RN, MPH, PhD, Berkeley, CA
Letty Lie, RN, MPH, Minneapolis, MN
Joyce Rezin, RN, MS, PNP, San Diego, CA

## Nutrition
**Catherine Cowell, PhD, Chair,** New York, NY
Annie Carr, MS, RD, Atlanta, GA
Darcy Eliades Graves, MPH, RD, Albany, OR
Janet Guidry, MPH, RD, New Orleans, LA
Mildred Monroe, MS, RD, LD, Atlanta, GA
Susan Schlosser, MS, RD, Chappaqua, NY
Denise Sofka, MPH, RD, Rockville, MD

## Prevention and Management of Child Abuse
**Anne B. Keith, DrPH, RN, C-PNP, Chair,** Portland, ME
Deborah E. Lowen, MD, FAAP, Tulsa, OK
Hannah Pressler, MHS, RN, CS, PNP, Portland, ME
Charles J. Schubert, MD, FAAP, Cincinnati, OH
Sara E. Schuh, MD, FAAP, Charleston, SC
John R. Stirling, Jr., MD, FAAP, Vancouver, WA

## Staff Health
**Iris Graville, RN, MN, Chair,** Lopez Island, WA
Judy Calder, RN, BSN, Oakland, CA
Susan Eckelt, CDA, Tulsa, OK
Rene Gratz, PhD, Milwaukee, WI
Jan Gross, RN, BSN, Greenbank, WA
Peggy King, RN, BSN, MFA, Seattle, WA
Lynn White, BA, Conyers, GA

## U.S. Department of Health and Human Services
Child Care Bureau
Moniquin Huggins, Washington, DC

### Maternal and Child Health Bureau
Phyllis Stubbs-Wynn, MD, MPH, Rockville, MD
Yolanda Baker, Rockville, MD
Lorraine Brown, RN, BS,Rockville, MD
Stephanie Bryn, MPH, Rockville, MD
David E. Heppel, MD, FAAP, Rockville, MD
Mark Nehring, DMD, MPH, Rockville, MD
Bonnie Strickland, PhD, Rockville, MD

## National Resource Center for Health and Safety in Child Care* Project Team

Marilyn Krajicek, EdD, RN, FAAN - Director
Shannon Collins, RN, BSN, MSCIS - Former Health Consultant
William Freud, MBA - Assistant Vice Chancellor -
    Information Systems, University of Colorado Health
    Sciences Center
Barbara Hamilton, MA - Assistant Director
Patricia Hartman, Research Assistant
Kristin Henslee, MLIS, Research Assistant
David Merten, BS - Fellow
Gerri Steinke, Ph.D - Research Associate
Virginia Torrey, BA - Program Specialist
Carol Vojir, PhD - Evaluator
Joy Wu, PhD - Fellow

* Based at the University of Colorado Health Sciences Center School of Nursing.

## Additional Contributors

Duane Alexander, MD, FAAP; National Institute of Child Health and Human Development, MD

Martha Anderson, BS, MA; Department of Health and Human Services; AK

Donna Blum-Kemelor, MS, RD, LD; Food and Nutition Service, USDA, VA

J. Patrick Byrne; National Association for Regulatory Administration, NJ

Michelle M. Canfield, RN, BSN, CCHC ; East Carolina University Greenville, NC

Ann Carmody, BS, Bureau of Regulation and Licensing, Wisconsin Department of Health and Family Services, WI

Anna Carter; Division of Child Development, NC

Susan A. Case, BA; Department of Human Services, Division of Child Care, OK

Sally Ann Clausen, ARNP, BSN; Healthy Child Care Iowa, Department of Public Health, IA

Patricia S. Cole, MPH; Healthy Child Care Indiana, Indiana Institute on Disability and Community-Early Childhood Center, IN

Judy Collins, MS; National Association for Regulatory Administration and National Child Care Information Center, OK

Colorado Department of Human Services; State of Colorado's Division of Child Care, CO

Ron Coté, PE; National Fire Protection Association, MA

Kathryn G. Dail, RN, BSN, MEd; Division of Public Health, NC

Ann Ditty, MA; Department of Health and Senior Services, MO

Susan Eckelt, CDA; National Association for Family Child Care, OK

Vincent L. Ferrandino, PhD; National Association of Elementary School Principals, VA

Richard Fiene, PhD; Pennyslvania State University, PA

Jacki Fling; General Services Administration, CO

Marsha A. Gates, MEd; Child Care Licensing Section, Office of Regulatory Services, Department of Human Resources, GA

Bethany Geldmaker, PNP, PhD; Department of Health, VA

Danette Glassy, MD, FAAP; American Academy of Pediatrics, IL

Lorrie Grevstad, RN, MN; Healthy Child Care Washington, Department of Health, WA

Joy Guenther; General Services Administration, CO

William Hager; United States Association for Child Care, ME

Michelle Hahn, RN, PHN, BSN; Healthy Child Care Minnesota, MN

Judy Hall, MS, RN, CS; Healthy Child Care New Jersey, Department of Health and Senior Services, NJ

Tanya D. Hauf, RN, CCHC; Child Care Resource and Referral, ND

Bruce Hershfield; Child Welfare League of America, Washington, DC

Kay Hollestelle; Children's Foundation, Washington, DC

Lisa Jordre, BS; Office of Child Care Services, SD

Pauline Koch, MS; National Association for Regulatory Administration, DE

Howard Maupin; General Services Administration, CO

Ellen T. Meyer; American Public Health Association, Washington, DC

Susan Metz, MEd; Department of Human Services, NJ

Shelly Meyer, RN,C, BSN; Healthy Child Care Montana, MT

Gwen Morgan, MS; Wheelock College Institute for Leadership and Career Initiative, MA

Kathi E. Morgan; ASTM International, PA

Sarah Mulligan, MEd; Division of Early Childhood, MT

Rose Marie Oliphant; Child Care in Health Care, TX

Nancy Norris; General Services Administration, CO

Katherine Otto; Healthy Child Care Georgia, GA

Konnie Parke, RN; Utah Healthy Child Care America, Department of Health, UT

Kathy Penfold, MSN, RN; Department of Health and Senior Services, MO

Genie Prewitt, RN, BSN; Formerly with Healthy Child Care Kentucky, KY

Jacqueline Quirk, RN, BSN; North Carolina Child Care Health and Safety Resource Center, NC

Lucy Roberts, Chief Consultant of Early Childhood for North Carolina; National Association of Early Childhood Specialists in State Departments of Education, NC

Marta T. Rosa, MEd; National Association of Child Care Resource and Referral Agencies, Washington, DC

Linda Satkowiak, ND, RN, CNS; Healthy Child Care Colorado, CO

Jacqueline W. Stewart; National Association for Sick Child Day Care, AL

Steve Shuman, BS; Department of Public Health, MA

Susan Smiley-Green, RN; North Jersey Community Coordinated Child Care Agency, Inc, NJ

Katherine Duchen Smith, RN, MS, CPNP; National Association of Pediatric Nurse Practitioners, CO

Patricia M. Spahr, MA; National Association for the Education of Young Children, Washington, DC

Carolynne H. Stevens; Division of Licensing Programs, Department of Social Services, VA

Barbara Thompson, MS; Office of Children and Youth, Military Community and Family Policy, Washington, DC

Donna Thompson, PhD; National Program for Playground Safety, IA

Lynne Torpy, RD; Department of Public Health and Environment, CO

Karen C. Williams, PhD; University of Wyoming, WY

In a project of such scope, many individuals provide valuable input to the end product. We would like to acknowledge those individuals whose names may have been omitted.

# INDEX

## A

Dust 87, 134

# E

E. coli 0157.H7 50, 55
Early childhood education 8
    degree 7, 82
Early Childhood Education Linkage System 139
Earthquakes 67
    evacuation plan 119
Eating 22, 34, 37
    problems 30, 134
    See also Family style meal service; Food
        service
Eating utensils 54, 89
ECELS. See Early Childhood Education Linkage
System
Ectoparasites. See Head lice; Scabies
Edison Electric Institute 139
EDITH. See Exit drill in the home
Education coordinators 7
    qualifications 7
Education. See Continuing education; Early
childhood education; Health education;
Qualifications under specific positions; Training
Educational leave. See under Leave
EEO. See Equal Employment Opportunity Act
Egg products 66
Eggs 66, 121
Electric space heaters. See Heating equipment
Electrical cords 62
Electrical fixtures and outlets 74, 75
    safety covers 74
Electrotechnical Laboratory 72
Emergency contact 16, 25, 44, 84
Emergency exits. See under Exits
Emergency medical services 12, 44, 45, 57, 60,
127
    See also Urgent medical care
Emergency Medical Services for Children
National Resource Center 139
Emergency plans 44, 119
    for children with special needs 13, 46, 117,
        123
    See also Evacuation of children
Emergency procedures 2, 5, 9, 13, 16, 25, 44, 45,
117
Emergency rooms 119
Emergency shelter 70, 71, 119
Emotional abuse. See under Child abuse
Employee pay. See Compensation and benefits
Employee turnover. See Turnover
Employment history 4

EMS. See Emergency medical services
Encapsulated asbestos. See under Asbestos
Enforcement of regulations. See under
Regulations
Enrollment
    immunization documentation 32
    policies 52
    pre-admission information 108, 122, 123
    procedures 118, 122
Enteric infections 107
Entrapment risks 69, 80
    in cribs 90
    in play equipment 95, 96
Environmental hazards. See specific types (e.g.
Radon, Lead Poisoning, etc.)
Environmental Protection Agency 75, 79, 86, 139
EPA. See Environmental Protection Agency
Epilepsy 46, 47, 114
Epinephrine 12, 60
Equipment 87, 96
    contamination of 42
    placement of 23
    safety of 80, 81
    See also Adaptive equipment and specific
        types (e.g. Cribs, Play
        equipment, etc.)
Erythromycin 51
ETL. See Electrotechnical laboratory
Evacuation of children
    children with special needs 70
    drills 119, 120
    plan 16, 119, 120, 126
    See also Emergency plans
Evaluation
    of a child 49
    of a child with special needs 112
    of staff. See under Staff
    of training 8
Excavations 69
Exclusion 9, 32
    of children 49, 50, 57, 108
        in facilities for ill children 54
    of staff 52
    policies 5, 49, 51, 117
Exercise
    excessive 28
    rings 95
Exhaust systems 77
Exits 69, 70, 71, 72, 98, 114, 120
    emergency 69, 72
Exploitation 45
Exposure control plan 15

# Stepping Stones to Using Caring for Our Children:
## National Health and Safety Performance Standards